THE POWER OF PERFUME

SUE PHILLIPS

THE POWER OF PERFUME

HOW TO CHOOSE IT, WEAR IT & ENJOY IT!

Publisher: Central Park South Publishing
www.centralparksouthpublishing.com

Design by Olivia Croom Hammerman (Indigo: Editing, Design, and More)

First Edition

ISBN 978-1-7363134-3-5

Dedicated to the two most important women in my life

To my beautiful mother Grace Phillips, a true "Renaissance Woman"—a talented artist, singer, musician, and home designer, whose style reflected her grace and cultured taste in everything she touched, and who instilled in me an appreciation and love for the arts.

She truly epitomized her name! (www.2marvelous4words.com)

For my lovely daughter, Romy Alexandra, a Peace Corps Volunteer (Moldova); Fulbright Scholar (Bucharest) who empowers individuals around the world and advocates for human rights and youth leadership development.

I am so proud of her and I know she's changing the world... while I am making it smell great!

Experience more sensuality and beauty through

The Power of Perfume

Confidence, romance and scentuality in a bottle

Contents

A brief history of perfume

The French perfected it!

Fragrance through the Decades

It's all about the ingredients

Perfume is about Romance, Sex, Sensuality

Where to wear a perfume?

Your personal notes: Create your own

Iconic people who wore distinctive perfumes.

Introduction

Have you ever walked down the street and you suddenly stop in your tracks because you encounter a familiar fragrance? Perhaps a scent wafting in the air reminds you of the memory of your first kiss? Or the whiff of baby powder immediately takes you back to a beautiful newborn? Do the iconic perfumes of Chanel #5 and Shalimar remind you of your grandmother?

Unlike our other senses, we cannot turn off our sense of smell, and it is the strongest link to memories, even more than sight and sound. So, during an event that is emotionally charged, what you smell at that moment becomes intimately intertwined with the experience. Scents can bring back the past or can set the mood for new experiences. That is because the limbic system houses the olfactory hub, the part of the brain that allows you to smell. When you process a smell, you're also processing the event or the emotion that goes with it.

This has happened to me several times where I live in Manhattan, and every now and again I will have an 'olfactive moment' and suddenly I smell an aroma that takes me back to my childhood in South Africa, (many decades earlier!) where for example, I encounter a certain scent that reminds me of our annual trips to the Game Reserve. In the pre-dawn 'safari rides,' the confluence of the aromas of the rich red earth scorched from the previous day's burning sun melding with the crisp aroma of the early morning dew on dry blades of grass … ah! So fresh, intoxicating, pungent and memorable! One day I'll bottle it!

This book is a compilation of my love of perfume and the answers given to the numerous questions asked by so many people who are fascinated by this marvelous subject, of how to choose it, where to wear it, and the many fragrance lovers I have met over the years whom I know will enjoy it. I hope you discover the magic and mystery of this extraordinary and powerful sense as you come with me on this fragrance journey.

There are a myriad of quotes about fragrance throughout the book, but as Coco Chanel famously said:

"A woman who doesn't wear perfume has no future."

I believe, as many women in the beauty industry before me have, that fragrance can change your life. I know! It sounds a bit of an over-promise. But it isn't. Having had over 40 years of experience in this industry, forty years of studying, marketing and creating memorable perfumes for iconic companies, and presenting innovative, interactive, fun, educational and scentertaining® bespoke perfume experiences, I can say, with some certainty, I know the power of perfume. I have been involved in the creation of major perfumes for iconic brands such as ***Tiffany*** and ***Society by Burberry***, as well as ***Trish McEvoy,*** and home fragrances for ***AVON***, ***Diane von Furstenberg,*** and I have witnessed, up close and personal, how fragrance notes and the alchemy of mixing them can change moods, emotions and realities.

Every time you experience and wear a fragrance that suits you, one that elevates your mood, that adds to your pleasure, that fascinates you, that expresses you, you are having a magical experience. That magical experience is subconsciously inspiring you, beautifying you, and strengthening you by increasing your happiness quotient and celebrating the goodness and wonders of life. In other words, you are gaining self confidence in your own powers of creating magic and beauty, simply by expressing yourself through a 'scentual' accent... drop by drop.

Perhaps your grandmother dabbed on Chanel No. 5 when she went out on Saturday evenings, and probably her friends did too! It is hard to believe that this iconic 'parfum du jour' is 100 years old. Even though the actual formula has changed over the years, this eternal scent is still the symbol of luxury and femininity, but at the time it was launched in 1921 it revolutionized the way women would smell, embodying the 'modern woman' that Coco Chanel wanted to epitomize.

Women then began wearing perfumes daily and using them to suit their moods and, now, perfume has become a staple of one's beauty regime. Every designer has a range of perfume offerings; celebrities endorse all kinds of perfumes, their own and designers'; and a variety of smaller, niche perfume companies are bringing an assortment of perfumes and fragranced home products to market, quicker and sometimes more creatively, than the large Corporations like Estee Lauder or L'Oreal, and these smaller artisanal brands are eventually bought out or acquired by a larger entity to gain more widespread distribution.

Perfume is big business now, upwards of $40 billion per year.

Perfume is the silent accessory that has become as important as the fashion outfits we wear, and that those interested in being original and unique are searching for their signature scent; one that reflects their individuality and personality, and that reminds them of who they really are, never mind those who meet them informally. If a piece of jewelry visually communicates our aesthetic, a scent does the same, even more clearly, through smell, one of the most powerful and emotional of our senses.

Since our sense of smell is so developed and evocative, I have noticed that women and men who ***really*** know themselves, who are confident and who want to be respected, want to wear fragrances that authentically reflect who they are, and to leave a scent trail that makes others stop and think, "Oh what is he or she wearing? I would love to know that person." Those people are not looking for the latest fad or celebrity scent, or the cheapest priced perfume. No 'flavor of the month' for them!

Even though perfume is intangible, it is powerful in its delicacy and distinctiveness; it is an elixir that creates beauty and lifts our spirits. If you are discerning and an arbiter of taste and one who understands the power of fragrance, you will agree that quality ingredients in a perfume are what you are constantly searching for. That does not necessarily mean the most expensive perfume, but it does mean the perfume that reflects the best part of you, that enhances you, that makes you feel alluring, beguiling and seductive. There is no doubt in my mind that Delilah who mesmerized Samson, and Salome who danced the Dance of the Seven Veils, and Cleopatra and other legendary women throughout history wore scents that were part of their allure. I don't believe that will ever change. As long as men and women continue to enhance their lives by making themselves more desirable, passionate, sexier and vibrant through all the senses—through harmonious music, through vivid paintings and exquisite clothes, through indulging in aromatic wines and feasting on savory delicacies, luscious edibles and experiencing the tactile hedonistic pleasure of attraction, they will enhance their lives through the poetic and meaningful power of a scent. Those are the people who know how essential and necessary fragrance has become.

The world is moving more towards personalization in products, since we all now want to express ourselves individually, and technology enables us to do more and more of that through the ubiquitous taking of 'selfies' and the ability of developing our own brand persona. A significant part of my work is creating personalized fragrances for those who understand the power of a signature fragrance that literally represents their psychological and spiritual profile. They know it will enhance themselves and complement those around them.

The human nose is a sensitive organ that can sense up to 350,000 different scents. It is our most powerful sense after our sense of sight and is directly connected to our memory through scent receptors in our nose, which are linked to the part of our brain correlated with memory and emotions. Research on scent aroma is being done to examine the productivity of the workplace and to assist with health and medical issues. Businesses from all over are examining different scents to trigger their customers to engage in an emotion that attracts them; to return to resorts and hotels, to purchase more products and more importantly to label their brand with a certain scent, also known as scent-branding. Perfume is both a Science and an Art and it continues to fascinate and intrigue.

Let's begin our odyssey into the infinitely seductive and magical 'scentual' world of fragrance, scent, perfume and aroma. Whatever you call it, come join me now, in these next pages, for what I hope you will discover is a scentertaining® journey where we explore priceless nuggets about the history of perfume, some home truths about perfume, some of the secrets of the magic and healing properties of perfume, how, where and when to wear it, and the myriad ways you can celebrate life and your senses, drop by drop, through the power of perfume!

Scentfully,

Sue Phillips

Scentrepreneur®
New York, New York

Testimonials

"Sue Phillips is at the top of her game with this book, with her entrepreneurial background and her seasoned understanding of the human condition!"

—Jeffrey Banks, Designer

"Sue Phillips is a true artist when it comes to creating fragrance that reflects the personality of the person wearing it. She has a gift unlike anything I've seen before, and her fragrances are divine."

—Elin Barton, Business Builder

"Sue has a true understanding of fragrance and how it impacts the scenes. With her personalized custom perfumes, she creates the perfect scent just for you."

—Raoul H Didisheim, Didisheim Consulting

"A unique business that gives you the opportunity to create your own scent."

—Alice Dow, Heart Tones

"Sue is fabulous! She is very informative, and the fragrance experience is one of a kind. You feel even more luxurious and decadent than you would imagine! It's a big confidence builder, knowing you have a fragrance that's uniquely yours!"

—Wanda Ellett, G45 Consulting

"A true professional with outstanding sensory talents!"

—Annette Green, Author/Fragrance Historian

"Sue Phillips is a Magnificent creative and innovative woman. Her creativity is a testimonial to the industry and recognized and celebrated by Hollywood Celebrities. She is in my book a total 10; highly recommend her."

—Petronely Grindea, Life Botanica

"Sue is an expert on Scent and fragrances. Her company is a fun interactive way to express yourself through creating your very own fragrance. I really enjoyed the process and learned so much from Sue! I highly recommend Sue and The Scentarium!"

—Betsy Karp, The Color Coach

"Leave it to fragrance creator extraordinaire to develop the loveliest and chicest perfumes. Sue Phillips puts together high and low notes of various scents. This way each client gets her very own fragrance and it becomes a signature scent."

—Shirley Kennedy, Fashion Art Bank Inc., Author

"Sue knows aromas and how they function with individuals."

—Louis Nelson, The Office of Louis Nelson

"Sue has been and is a rare caring, dedicated and knowledgeable professional. I would highly recommend her... and I am very impressed with what she has accomplished in building the Scentarium. Very creative and adds spark to our industry."

—Richard Panzarasa, Panzarasa Group Inc.

"Sue Phillips is the real deal! An Industry Pioneer and amazing entrepreneur."

—Alyssa Peek, Peek Photography

"Sue Phillips is the premier custom fragrance designer. She is always gracious, professional and kind. She can guide you to create the most perfect perfume for you. Planning a time to be at The Scentarium will give you a unique experience. You can do it on your own or share with dear friends or family."

—Robin Scarella PR & Special Events

"I was recently taken through one of Sue's experiences. I was fascinated and blown away by how this new approach leads you to a deeper to understanding of yourself through scent. I highly recommend her and Scentarium."

—Jaye Smith, Breakwater Consulting

"SUE is very devoted to the creation of marvelous and unique scents. Her knowledge of the "notes" and how she teaches you how to put them together is unparalleled."

—Ricky Smithline, CENTURY 21 Metropolitan

"So special and unique. Sue delights everyone who meets her with her charm, customer service and extraordinary personalized fragrances!"

—Mark Tamayo, Mark Tamayo Design

"I fell in love with a perfume years ago, the 1st Tiffany Perfume, created by Sue Phillips, my "game on" & sexy amplifier perfume. I had only drops left in my bottle of 20 plus years, which is no longer available. Then one day I was blessed in 2018 to meet Sue Phillips & get her as a client in one of my businesses I co-founded called IC Genius! The best gift I got in Jan. 2020, pre Covid 19, was having Sue host a perfume experience at one of my company's retreats. It was individually amazing to create our own perfumes! I called mine "Angel Wings". I use it on special occasions and am always showing women how beautiful the scent & exclusive atomizers are. Every woman should have her own experience & custom perfume, made by her for her, aren't you worth it? I am! I felt Sue's love & commitment to our experiences being the most critical thing to her as she pampered us with her knowledge & attention. I am now bringing this experience to a new level of business & the program I have created for Career Women, as part of their team building journey. Thank you Sue for creating an experience and a scent that fueled my passions, my game on moments, my love for people & angels, and knowing that I was so blessed to meet you after all these years, being a fan of your Tiffany "genius. For those men & partners out there, get this for your special one; nothing can beat this as a gift and/or do it for yourself."

—Letty Valez Founder IC Genius

"Sue is extremely knowledgeable about everything that goes into making a signature fragrance—and a scent that smells divine with your individual pheromones and body chemistry! I gave her skill to my then-fiancé as an engagement present! He now smells deliciously appealing to me!"

—Christina Weppner, Architect

"I attended an exclusive workshop which was like a fairytale. I definitely recommend The Scentarium for a luxurious bespoke experience."

—Peter Zakian Relationship Builder

"Sue has excellent Industry experience and a great nose!!"

—Jean, Zimmerman, JHZ creative management

Grace notes: the power of beauty

There are four things admirable for a woman to be, at any age! It's always wonderful to be elegant, it's always fashionable to have grace, it's always glamorous to be brave, and it's always important to own a delectable perfume! Yes, wearing a beautiful fragrance is in style at any age!

—C. JoyBell C.

GRACE is a very meaningful word to me and, to my delight, in researching it for this book, there are many different interpretations of it, most of which I knew, and others, came as a surprise: "a special favor; an act of kindness; a charming trait or characteristic; ease and suppleness of movement; as a title of address for a duke, duchess or archbishop; a short prayer at a meal asking for a blessing or giving thanks; three sister goddesses in Greek mythology (The Three Graces), a musical trill, a sense of propriety, and the quality or state of being considerate". The surprise was the addition of the "Five Graces" which also refers to an Eastern concept—the **five graces** of ***sight, sound, touch, smell, and taste,*** each of which needs to be honored in the full experience of life, and to which I subscribe and celebrate daily, in my work.

The word resonates with me for all the above reasons, but most specifically, GRACE was my mom's name, which she epitomized. She was beautiful, dignified, elegant, polished, refined, poised, had great style and dexterity, was a most talented South African artist and calligrapher, singer, musician, home decorator, and excelled in cooking and baking. From her, I get my love of the arts, music and flair for cooking. While I cannot paint, I am thankful every day to her for instilling in me an appreciation for art, music, dance and cooking—all the senses which I honor every day, and which are connected to our sense of smell. My inherent love of fragrance has therefore been in my DNA for a long time, and I am passionate about the beauty of our most powerful sense. Thankyou Mom! Graceful always

Perfume is instant poetry.

Poems ...are perfume bottles momentarily unstopped—what they release is volatile and will vanish, and yet it can be released again.

—Jayne Hirshfield

A poem evokes. A poem teases our memory. A poem arouses strong emotions because of its beauty.

Perfumers of course know this and sometimes they name perfumes accordingly: **Poême** by Lancôme. (Contrasts of bitter and sweet to create a special sensual aura); and **Vol de Nuit**, (Night Flight 1933 by Jacques Guerlain.) Vol de Nuit is dedicated to adventurous women who nourished their passion for risk-taking and knew how to claim their place in a man's world without losing their femininity! **Vent Vert** (Green Wind by Balmain **is** a synesthete's dream: It smells like the color green)**. L'air de Temps** by Nina Ricci (The Air of Time or "the current trend") or **Un Jardin sur le Nil** by Hermès (A Garden on the Nile) an impressionistic stroll through the island-gardens on the Nile at Aswan, the starting point for a new olfactory adventure. All these names evoke an image that is an escape from our office, our bills, our car repairs and our daily routines. Perfume speaks of something ephemeral, the wind, gardens, trysts, beauty, forgotten love. When you wear a beautiful perfume, it 'becomes' you, it envelops you, its beauty is transported along with you, it reflects who you are, and everyone around you will smell it, and for a moment they will be transported from their daily responsibilities to somewhere deeper, freer and essential to the health of the soul. You are giving those around you a gift by wearing it. In that second of contact with your scent, you are reminding them of beauty.

A genie unleashes dreams from a bottle. So, can you.

What do I wear in bed? Why, Chanel No.5 of course.
—Marilyn Monroe

Perfume is a most powerful invisible accessory. The physical action of applying a perfume from a bottle, whether it is dabbled, sprayed or splashed is a delicate and marvelous ritual that has been performed for centuries. How, where and when to apply perfume is a question I am frequently asked and shall reveal the answers in the following pages. A perfume bottle is a tangible, exquisite "objet d'art" and can enhance a mediocre perfume or can elevate a fragrance to become a classic and make it even more precious.

Chanel No. 5 was housed in a plain rectangular, slightly masculine bottle, a minimal laboratory 'flask' with black sans serif text emblazoned on a white label, stamped with a bold number. This is the famous No.5 bottle that was designed by Mademoiselle Gabrielle "Coco" Chanel. From her earliest days, the number five had potent associations for her (esteemed as signifying the pure embodiment of a thing), especially its spirit, its mystic meaning. In 1920, when presented with small glass vials containing sample scents numbered 1 to 5 and 20 to 24 for her assessment, she chose the fifth vial. Chanel told her master perfumer, Ernest Beaux, whom she had commissioned to develop a new fragrance, "I present my dress collections on the fifth of May, the fifth month of the year and so we will let this sample number five keep the name it has already, it will bring good luck." It became a symbol of the modernity she wanted to reflect for her perfume. The other reason she chose the 5th scent was because of its modern ingredient, aldehyde[1] (a very new crisp molecule which when combined with the other floral ingredients gave it a 'newness'. In fact, the story is that the perfumer's assistant put too much aldehyde in the formula, so it became the most profitable "mistake" in perfume history!

The word aldehyde was coined by Justus von Liebig as a contraction of the Latin alcohol dehydrogenatus (dehydrogenated alcohol).

By 1959 the bottle had joined the permanent collection at the New York Museum of Modern Art. Andy Warhol made it the subject of nine screen prints five years later, catapulting it to 20th-century icon. Since 1921 when it was launched, the iconic No.5 bottle has been reinterpreted and modified eight times to meet the aesthetic criteria of the era. Interestingly, the double CC first appeared on the stopper in the original version only to be dropped before reappearing in the 1970s.

Perfume bottles have certainly become an art form and Museums around the world display ancient perfume bottles. Glass blowers created unique, one of a kind glass bottles. Today, glass manufacturers produce large quantities of glass bottles through automation. People love to keep their empty perfume bottles and display them as works of art on their dressing table. However what you release onto yourself is something very different: fleeting, intangible, a trail of something that cannot be seen nor touched, something that speaks a language,

1 An aldehyde */ˈældɪhaɪd/* is a compound containing a functional group with the structure –CHO, consisting of a carbonyl center (a carbon double-bonded to oxygen) and also bonded to hydrogen. The word aldehyde was coined by Justus von Liebig as a contraction of the Latin alcohol dehydrogenatus (dehydrogenated alcohol

like music, not of words, but connects 'scentually' and deeply with your dreams and the dreams of those around you. Only the "sillage" or trail of the perfume lingers, and the empty decorative bottle are the remains of the promises it held.

A greeting can be so memorable.

Perfume is that last and best reserve of the past, the one which when all our tears have run dry, can make us cry again!

—Marcel Proust

A fleeting "hello" or "goodbye" kiss can turn into a significant and memorable moment as you literally inhale someone's scent. If it is pleasant, you may embrace a little longer to continue the enchanting aromatic encounter or, conversely, immediately feel repelled and recede if the scent is off-putting. When you pass someone on a street, or walk into a room, you change the conversation. For one split second, the other takes in your scent and, for that moment they are transported elsewhere. As to what you feel when wearing a scent, as you spray or dab it on yourself, you are reminded that the aura you project intertwines with your chemistry. You are committed to it. As Dostoyevsky said, "Beauty saves." And by having a graceful, evocative scent, you are enlivening the souls of others, not just yourself.

Only something ephemeral creates true mystery.

If someone wears a scent, and it truly reflects his or her personality, there is usually a positive reaction from those around them. However, if it really doesn't, the subliminal reaction might be "Why did he or she choose to wear that?" Wearing a fragrance attracts attention and tells us, and others, something about ourselves. It draws attention. The wearer can do it in a quiet, mysterious way, which elicits a query: Who are they? It encourages people to get a little closer and draws us in. A 'loud' highly commercial fragrance might suggest something very different as in 'shouting' or wearing inappropriate sparkly clothes to a funeral. Giving us just a whiff of beauty is like a hint of mystery; it encourages us to want more and to get to know that person better.

You may leave the room,
but your trail won't.

The smell of perfume left behind. There's not a word for it in English.
—John Green

"Sillage" (pronounced SEE-YAHJ) is the French word for the perfume trail left in the air when someone leaves the room, similar to the 'wake' of a boat or the track of waves that it makes behind it as it moves through the water. It is the scent that lingers, when the person disappears, and therefore the person really has not gone. Those who are left in the room are assailed by a question. Who was that? "Sillage" is often mentioned in French or Russian romantic novels. Men would be intoxicated by the aroma and want to follow it. Perfumes today are not as strong as they once wore, since FDA rules disallowed and then banned certain ingredients in fragrances, known as allergens which are deemed carcinogenic. Sadly, some of the most characteristic ingredients have been banned such as **coumarin**, which gives tonka bean (similar to vanilla) its distinct flavor. It's been banned in the United States since 1954 because it can cause liver problems in high concentrations, so synthetic, lighter versions have been formulated. Some restaurants banned women from wearing ***Giorgio Beverly Hills*** in the 1980's when it was popular, since it was so overpowering! (and it was!) That being said, there is still something in the allure of a scent that just slightly lingers to touch the senses. The true perfume lover searches for a signature scent that retains that allure and sillage. It can be subtle yet still convey a powerful message of reflecting the wearer's individuality.

A quality perfume brings quality into a room.

What is 'quality' in a perfume? The definition of quality *is* ***"the standard of something as measured against other things of a similar kind; the degree of excellence of something."***

In the same way that we measure "quality" in food and fabric: e.g. organic foods are perceived as better quality than non-organic processed foods; and natural fabrics such as cashmere, wool, cotton are better quality than polyester which is essentially plastic, not biodegradable, and provides poor insulation. In perfume, there is a huge difference between the quality of ingredients, which are made from natural ingredients versus synthetic formulations. It is true that some synthetic fragrances last longer because of the fixatives, increasing their tenacity and staying power. Is it possible to smell expensive? I believe so. When we were creating the Tiffany perfume, the overarching objective was to create a perfume of quality, reflecting the ethos of the brand, and the finest ingredients were used.

What's the difference between expensive and 'cheap' perfumes?

Some perfumes may contain rare flower petals or ingredients which are difficult to obtain as they are only harvested at certain times of the year. And the more essential oils a perfume contains, the more expensive it usually is. (I will talk about differences in concentration later). It also takes unique packaging for a product to stand out. And this can be costly but it's not all vanity. High-end perfumes use thicker glass in unique shapes rather than thinner, stock bottles, and the color and brilliance of glass varies depending on its content. This makes them sturdier and more protective of the perfume. Some glass perfume bottles will have a green tinge and are heavier, while crystal is generally light in color and mostly translucent and 'sparkly.' Both cheap and expensive perfume bottles are made of glass, which is a generic name. Crystal is a subcategory of glass, made in the same manner as glass but with different materials. Hence, all crystal is glass, but not all glass is crystal. Similarly, the dispenser and cap on cheap perfumes is often plastic and poorly fitted which means the "juice" is exposed to air which will gradually adulterate and discolor the fragrance. On high-end fragrances, special care is taken to make sure the bottles are air-tight to preserve the ingredients. The shelf-life of quality perfumes can be 5 years or more. If your translucent, golden liquid takes on a more opaque, amber, darker hue, that could be a sign that it has passed its expiration date. When I evaluate fragrances, I can usually detect 'quality' in a nano-second. It is the difference between the luxurious soft, thick cashmere compared to thin, rough, acrylic, and I literally "see" and 'feel' the difference in the contrast between the smooth, roundness of a quality perfume versus the thin, linear, harshness of inferior ingredients.

Imitation perfumes tend to be cheaper to produce because they replicate mainly the top notes of a fragrance. Try comparing a fake with the real thing after 3 hours, and the cheap perfume may lose its smell after an hour or two, or have very little smell at all. Similarly, cheaper perfumes that aren't fake may have only a single note or top note, and are not as 'complex' as fine perfumes. If they do have medium or base notes, they won't be as pleasant or as sophisticated as the more expensive fragrances. Common base notes in more expensive fragrances include patchouli, vanilla, sandalwood, amber, oakmoss, which gives perfume its lasting impression.

Some not-too-expensive scents have that sophistication –probably because the ingredients might be redolent of rose and vanilla. Some 'niche' perfumes (usually marketed by smaller companies dedicated primarily to creating perfume, as opposed to perfume from large fashion and fragrance houses) might be too 'artsy'—just like a variety of innovative ingredients ala nouvelle cuisine. But if your scent represents quality, it communicates something perfect and tasteful, rather like adding just the right scarf or necklace to a simple black dress. Note that just because a scent is pricy doesn't mean it's necessarily better than a less costly one. No two people smell things the same way and no two perfumes or colognes will smell the same on your skin as it will another. Choose a scent that suits your budget, skin scent and your personality. A fragrance is all about reflecting your own uniqueness and making it yours! You'll never have to sing your own praises; your perfume will do it for you.

Wear perfume from the Bedroom to the Boardroom

I have known women (and men) who have worn the same "signature scent" for years and are bereft when it is discontinued. They find a fragrance they love; they wear it all the time and it comes to represent them, day and night, summer and winter… and they literally wear it from the bedroom to the boardroom. With thousands of fragrances available to them, they deem it a fragrance that reflects who they are and stay with it. They get compliments on it and it distinguishes them from others. A signature scent reflects who you are. So, when it is discontinued, or the formula changes, the wearer literally feels incomplete and he (yes, men too!) or she, is desperate to find it. We frequently get requests to duplicate beloved fragrances, and It always intrigues clients when I tell them that I was involved in the creation of the Tiffany perfume.

> **"Sue, I have used the same perfume for over twenty years, and unfortunately, it's been discontinued. I'm hopeful that you will be able to help me recreate it. I will be in New York this Monday. Is there a time that we can meet? It was actually a cologne that I wore—the old Tiffany cologne. I still have one more bottle boxed up in the refrigerator. Many thanks" —Helen G**

As mentioned above, some people wear their signature scent constantly: in the boardroom and the boudoir, and throughout the seasons. That scent probably incorporates both their sensuality and their individuality. Some people, however, do wear different scents at different times and for different occasions. The most requested type of fragrance I receive from American men and women, is for a "fresh and clean" fragrance. And when I explain that 'Fresh' could mean the scent of refreshing sparkling lemons, or freshly new-mown cut grass; the breezy smell of the ocean, the falling rain after a scorching hot day, or the refreshing crisp scent of mountain air, they stop to really think about it and begin to understand that fragrance is a complex art. They might prefer a refreshing, spirited crisp fragrance for day, and for night might want something sultrier, more sensual, more provocative. Some people combine their own concoction. Sadly, in the last few years many companies frown on the use of fragrance in the workplace because it seems there have been so many complaints of people getting headaches and allergies. My response to that is to think about the comparison of quality fragrances to wine or champagne—drinking cheap champagne or inferior wine will guarantee a hangover the next day because of the sulphates and chemicals. So back to the subject of quality!

I believe that wearing fragrance is an essential part of your wardrobe and much like complementing your outfit with certain accessories such as scarves, belts, jewelry and other accessories, fragrance is a silent, yet powerful accessory and wearing it completes the outfit. If your signature fragrance reflects who you are, and you really love to wear it, even though it might not be 'appropriate' for work, my recommendation is to understand the corporate culture in which you work, and yet still be true to who you are as well. One wouldn't wear a formal outfit in the playground or tennis court, so a very sensual and provocative fragrance in the boardroom might not be appropriate. You might wear a lighter version of your favorite perfume in the form of a body lotion which is not as strong as perfume. However, reflecting your individuality with a signature scent promotes confidence, and we all want to be that, not only in the bedroom. Fragrances speak their silent language and the true "Scentualist" believes in creating a statement everywhere he or she goes.

Smell is distinctly linked to the brain's emotion.

Many of us have experienced the scent of freshly baked chocolate chip cookies, or the aroma of vanilla wafting from the kitchen to sell a house or an apartment. It gives potential buyers the feeling of comfort and nostalgia and reminds us of the "good old days." It can sway a homebuyer to spend time in a space during an open house, which fosters positive emotions, and ultimately is the reason they purchase the property. The smell of hot bread to lure people into a food store or restaurant triggers childhood memories of mom baking in the kitchen. However, these days when it comes to choosing a scent to permeate your home, you might forget the conventional wisdom about freshly baked cookies, because it might trigger negative emotions as mom works full-time and has NEVER baked cookies!

A counter argument is the advice of professionals like Eric Spangenberg, Dean of the University of California, Irvine Paul Merage School of Business. He cautions against using complex or mingled scents, because his research suggests that "people can be distracted by a mixture of smells, they subconsciously spend a portion of their cognitive energy trying to identify the scent". I think it is very alluring to experience a mixture of aromas—it helps us to differentiate and understand which ones appeal to us and which don't.

Our sense of smell is the second strongest sense that we have after Sight, yet the most powerful according to Martin Lindstrom in his book "***Brand Sense.***" Sight is the strongest. Unlike other senses, we cannot turn off our sense of smell; we can close our eyes, choose not to touch, cover our ears, or close our mouth. Because of this, during an event that is emotionally charged, what you smell at the moment becomes intimately intertwined with the experience.

This is because the limbic system houses the olfactory hub, the part of the brain that allows you to smell and has direct connections to the two areas which connects memory and emotion: the amygdala and hippocampus. When you process a smell, you're also processing the event or the emotion that goes with it. As a result, scent and emotions become indelibly imprinted in your brain. A client told me that when he discovered his father's scarf when cleaning the attic, he recognized the scent his father wore, and became incredibly emotional because it brought back the memories of their difficult relationship. We all remember the smell of our grandmother's perfume. Some people love a baby's smell. Johnson's Baby Powder[2] was masterful in creating their universally recognized smell of their product so the baby and the mother would feel all cuddly with it. Perfume is no different ...smell goes right to one's emotions.

2 In 2018, a St. Louis jury ordered Johnson & Johnson to pay $4.7 billion to 22 women and their families who say the powder contributed to their ovarian cancer. A woman in California who says Johnson & Johnson baby powder caused her to develop mesothelioma was awarded $29 million.

When you can't smell, you usually can't taste either!

When nothing else subsists from the past, after the people are dead, after the things are broken and scattered...the smell and taste of things remain poised a long time, like souls... bearing resiliently, on tiny and almost impalpable drops of their essence, the immense edifice of memory.

—Marcel Proust

Losing one sense can create a diminished life, but imagine losing two? So many of us don't even give our sense of smell a second thought! Unless perhaps you smell a really foul odor, or you lose your sense of smell entirely. Not all of us are lucky enough to have all five senses. Look at poor Beethoven unable to hear, and yet how fortunate we are to have his glorious symphonies, piano sonatas, one opera, chamber works and string quartets! Thank goodness he did not lose more.

Losing your sense of smell, also means you can't taste. Much of our daily life and celebrations revolve around food i.e. meeting for breakfast, leisurely lunches, afternoon teas, exotic dinners, and family occasions such as Thanksgiving and Christmas Holidays. If you can't taste, it becomes difficult to socialize and people make excuses for not wanting to partake. Anosmia, sadly, is the partial or complete loss of the sense of smell. Common conditions that irritate the nose's lining, such as allergies or a cold, can lead to temporary anosmia. In the recent Covid19 pandemic, thousands of people have reported loss of smell and taste as symptoms of this deadly virus. More serious conditions that affect the brain or nerves, such as brain tumors or head trauma, can cause permanent loss of smell, and ultimately a diminution of life. if you can't taste food and savor delicious aromas, people literally retract and fade.

I had the distinct honor and pleasure of meeting with and interviewing Dr Robert Henkin, who is a physician dealing with taste and smell dysfunction and the Founder of the Taste and Smell Clinic; the Center for Molecular Nutrition and Sensory Disorders, in Washington, D.C. Dr. Henkin was a Professor of Neurology and Pediatrics at Georgetown University Medical Center. His career has been devoted to research, writing, and diagnosing and curing the problems associated with the loss of taste and smell that affect an estimated 21 million Americans. He told me that approximately 1 in 8 Americans over age 40 (up to 40 million people, or 12.4 percent of the population) have measurable smell dysfunction. Approximately 3 percent of Americans have anosmia (no sense of smell) or severe hyposmia (minimal sense of smell). Anosmia, also known as 'smell blindness', is the loss of the ability to detect one or more smells and may be temporary or permanent.

Smell and taste are two strong senses that work in harmony. The ability to taste something is highly influenced by one's ability to smell an aroma. Loss of smell and taste, through aging, viral issues or excessive smoking, often leads to a diminishment of appetite as eating food becomes less enjoyable. This can lead to depression and many other health problems. When we have a cold, we can't taste food and therefore can't smell, so losing one's sense of smell can lead to a less enjoyable lifestyle and some people retreat from society as a result. It proves how the scent-ual life is so important. I would venture to say that a person who has a very acute sense, such as an acute ear for music, will have an acute sense of taste and smell (given there is no illness.) It's as if being deeply involved in the senses enlivens all of them. So it is with perfume. If you scent yourself, you have awakened your senses and it will enhance all the others. An enhancement of one sense is perhaps an enhancement of all.

There are foods that help your sense of smell.

There are some simple home remedies to help restore these important senses.

Garlic helps restore the sense of smell and taste, clearing nasal congestion.

Cayenne Pepper also helps reduce nasal congestion.

Lemon, Grapefruit and Oranges are rich in vitamin C, an antioxidant that enhances the body's immunity to help fight diseases and infections.

Cinnamon's sweet smell can enhance your smelling power.

Zinc-rich foods like nuts and beans will improve your sense of smell and taste.

Keeping healthy is important and frequent use of Copper will help stop colds as viruses and bacteria are rapidly killed by copper[3] by direct contact and used within 3 hours after the first sign a cold is about to start. I recently discovered that using a Copper Zap the minute I feel a cold coming on, will help stop a cold.

---

3 American Society for Microbiology

Oysters are an aphrodisiac and they enhance the sense of smell!

The reason why oysters are considered an aphrodisiac is that the hormones that make the ovaries and testes are in part zinc-dependent, and hormones don't function very well without zinc. To boost your sense of smell try eating zinc rich foods which are also a great source of lean protein such as lobster, liver, lentils, sunflower seeds and pecans. Oysters are both sensual to eat as they are slippery, slurpy and slide down your throat and laden with zinc. They also help promote virility and Casanova supposedly consumed 50 oysters each day to keep his libido in top form. Oysters are often the prelude to a scentualist's favorite seduction scene, frequently ending in arousal and passionate love! (hmmmm!) Oysters—food from the gods!

Make sure you know how to care for your perfumes.

If you're not exactly sure if it's time to replace your perfumes, be sure to know how to store them—this will help guide you when looking to see if it's time to discard your current favorites or not. Fragrances, particularly Perfume and Eau de Parfum should be stored in cool, dark places and not exposed to direct sunlight, or very extreme temperatures, despite the myth that people should keep their fragrances in the fridge or near the windowsill, close to air conditioners or heaters . Fragrances should not be chilled, (unlike white wine,) as the extreme temperature will upset the natural ingredients' delicate balance which can be affected by extreme temperatures. Some argue that Cologne and Eau de Toilette with a higher concentration of alcohol may be stored in the frig, but I always advise against it, and scents with large amounts of alcohol will eventually evaporate.

If properly cared for, fragrances can last for up to five years. One of the signs of aging is discoloration. When a perfume has been opened and is exposed to air, it will become darker, and the smell will also change. So, if it was originally a light translucent golden color and over the years it looks like dark 'rum' color, it probably means it has expired and should not be worn.

The difference between Perfume, Cologne and Eau de Toilette.

If you've ever been stuck in an airport at the duty-free shop, chances are you've perused the fragrance section. And you probably noticed that they come in a lot of forms: Perfume, Eau de Parfum, Eau de Toilette, Cologne. So, what are the differences, you ask?

In short, all fragrances are a mixture of similar ingredients but at different concentrations or strengths: e.g. essential oils (originally extracted from nature such as flowers, herbs, spices, woods) are diluted with distilled water and perfumer's alcohol, (not regular alcohol) but they are differentiated and distinguished by the concentration of perfume oil in alcohol and water. Perfumers study for years to formulate perfumes, and depending on the concentration they choose to create, the fragrance can be stronger or lighter which explains why some last longer, are more expensive, and perform better, while others disappear after an hour or two. These days, synthetic ingredients are also used when natural ingredients are not available. Here is an explanation of the 5 different types of fragrances.

- **Perfume or Parfum** This is the most concentrated, expensive, strongest and most long-lasting of all fragrance options. It is composed of 20%—30% pure perfume oils. Perfumes are more concentrated and therefore the most expensive. A few drops used to last 12—24 hours. These days, probably only 6-8 hours. (why? Because the FDA has determined the concentration allowed to be used now). Perfume is much more precious and comes in smaller beautiful crystal glass bottles, sometimes with a beautiful glass 'wand' or stopper which is dabbed at the pulse points. Perfume can be sprayed, dabbed or splashed. With a high concentration of essential oil, you are likely to notice your fragrance working from morning to evening. People with sensitive skin may do better with perfumes (or parfums in French), as they have far less alcohol than other fragrance types and therefore are not as likely to dry out the skin.

- **Eau de parfum—EDP**—Less concentrated than Perfume and contains 15%—20% pure perfume oil and lasts for about four to six hours; can be sprayed or poured. No matter what the occasion is, this fragrance type also has a great diffusion and is less expensive than perfume.
- **Eau de Toilette—EDT**—has a fragrance concentration of between 5% to 15%, and is lighter, less expensive, and is one of the most popular lighter types of fragrance available. It will normally last two to three hours and is considered by some as daywear (while **EDP** is considered nightwear). This can also be sprayed or splashed. Literal translation is 'toilet water' and was used by the French ladies of the court which they sprayed or splashed to get themselves ready for their daily activities—also to refresh them in lieu of bathing! The term eau de toilette originates from the French term "faire sa toilette" which means literally means 'to get ready' or "to prepare her toilette' e.g. to wash!
- **Eau de cologne—Eau de cologne (EDC)** has a much lower fragrance concentration (about 2% to 4%) than **EDT** and with a higher alcohol content, is therefore cheaper than those above. It generally lasts for up to two hours. This is the oldest term for perfume, often used for masculine scents. Light, fresh and sporty and comes in bigger bottles. Also, it tends to be used in fragrances for younger people as it is very light. It was created

after a traditional recipe that used herb and citrus notes and originated in Cologne Germany.

- **NOTE:** Your grandfather or great grandfather might have worn the Original 4711 Eau de Cologne, named after its street address at Glockengasse No. 4711 in Cologne, Germany (which I visited a few years ago) and which was produced in 1799. It is one of the oldest, still produced fragrances in the world. *Eau de Cologne* or "cologne", has become a generic term which can be applied to perfume for men or women, but it conventionally refers to perfumes marketed toward men.
- **Eau Fraiche** is similar to **EDC** in that the scent will last for only an hour or two and has an even lower fragrance concentration of only 1% to 3%. While Eau Fraiche has a low fragrance concentration, it does not contain a high amount of alcohol, so this is also good for those with sensitive skin. It is the most diluted of all the fragrances, and literally means 'fresh water'—ideal for hot summer days.

Perfume is an Art & Science but also highly regulated

Do you sometimes wonder why the favorite perfume you've been wearing for years has either changed or is no longer available? There ae several reasons for this such as declining sales, difficulty in sourcing ingredients, or the Regulatory Bodies such as European Union and IFRA (International Fragrance Association) which have disallowed and banned certain ingredients such as Oakmoss, which is one of the defining parts of the family of perfumes known as ***Chypre***, and found in legendary perfumes as **Chanel No. 5; Miss Dior, Mitsouko**. Patchouli, which is now being included in the newer chypre families, has very different characteristics. Oak moss is the defining smoothness of a chypre.

They determined that two molecules found in oak moss and tree moss may cause an allergic skin reaction called dermatitis. Certain other ingredients have been banned as part of the 26 allergens as determined by the European Union. These include isoeugenol (which is found in ylang-ylang) and eugenol (found in cinnamon). Plus, linalool, found in lavender, and citrus materials such as bergamot. Citrus materials that contain any of these substances, or that oxidize on the skin, are considered potential allergens.

Can you believe that a Lavender allergy is caused by linalool which produces lavender's fragrance? The soothing, calming, relaxing beloved Lavender! On blog posts such as Fragrantica.com[4] fragrance lovers leave no doubt about their dissatisfaction about how their favorite perfumes have changed. I hear this all the time from my clients. They are not at all happy with changes to fragrance formulations and strong emotions are stirred among perfume devotees as you can read here:

angel6 06/26/19 20:09
I never heard of somebody dying from perfume allergy in my life. All I know is that I have repurchased Guerlain's Nahema and Jicky and they smell different now, I absolutely despise IFRA and corporate greed.

kingofengland 12/23/20 17:37
I think Luca Turin and Tania Sanchez do have a point. If a small minority of people find they are allergic to perfumes, they should stop using them, not deprive everyone else from using them. If they find tomatoes disagree with them, they should refrain from eating them, not ban tomatoes from consumption worldwide. A few people are dangerously allergic to penicillin, but nobody says penicillin should be withdrawn. The danger with organisations like IFRA is that they become over-powerful and have to find more and more things to ban, to justify their own existence.

TrephineArtist 06/25/19 03:38
IAs someone previously stated/hinted at, there's always going to be someone who's allergic to a certain ingredient. For example, in food some people have nut allergies, we can't just ban all nuts. Personally, I believe we will always be sold carcinogens as money talks, 20 years down the line certain things will be banned again to make it look like the powers that be (big business) care about us

UnearthlyApothecary 06/25/19 06:04
My opinion is, we live on a poisoned planet...everything from our food to our water supplies. I am no longer going to worry about it in perfume. I

4 Forbidden Smell is Sweet: IFRA and Fragrance Safety http://bit.ly/3qHeWni

think we need to get rid of the IFRA altogether and just list ingredients on the side of the packaging/bottle that says something like " list of possible allergens in this product (list of ingredients) wear at your own risk" people should be able to choose their poison ;)

euevabrown 06/24/19 00:57
We should fight to stop this IFRA organization! It is outrageous what they did with perfumes and soon we will pay a lot of money for WATER!!! After all who is allergic should not use perfume! It is not normal to change the perfumes world for few people who are allergic! After all, somebody could be lactose itolerant, so should all the dairy products be forbidden or changed for that??? And the cigarettes and alcohol are making far more victims than perfumes!!!

FDA: In just the same way that the FDA regulates a wide range of products, including foods (except for aspects of some meat, poultry and egg products, which are regulated by the U.S. Department of Agriculture); human and veterinary drugs; vaccines and other biological products; Fragrance ingredients in cosmetics must meet the same requirement for safety as other cosmetic ingredients. The law does not require FDA approval before they go on the market, but they must be safe for consumers when they are used according to labeled directions, or as people customarily use them.

IFRA: The International Fragrance Association IFFRA[5] is the official self-regulatory representative body of the fragrance industry worldwide. Its main purpose is to ensure the safety of fragrance materials through a dedicated science program. IFRA publishes a list of usage standards for fragrance materials, limiting or prohibiting the use of ingredients, based on the findings of the Research Institute of Fragrance Materials[6], which gathers data regarding the safety of fragrance materials.

5 International Fragrance Association IFFRA http://bit.ly/3iEJZgS

6 Research Institute of Fragrance Materials https://www.rifm.org/

You will see how complicated the Art of Perfumery is. Perfumers study thousands of ingredients and know which ingredients will combine to give a beautiful, long lasting perfume fragrance, cologne or eau de toilette.

Perfume Vocabulary

In general, the term fragrance, comes from the word **'fragrant'** which means "a pleasant, sweet scent." Therefore, any object associated with this word means anything that enhances the smell of another object to yours or others' liking. The words **'fragrance'** or **'scent'** can be used generically, and it can mean any particular smell.

Why do some words have a positive or negative connotation? I have always felt that the words ***perfume, fragrance, scent, aroma, bouquet, essence, cologne*** are 'positive' and reflects scents that are ***pleasant, sweet and fragrant***, and conversely, the words ***smell, odor, stink, stench, foul, reek,*** obviously connote a negative bias.

Beyond this list, there are even more kinds of fragrances and scented bath and body products, such as mists and aftershaves, deodorants, and body lotions, grooming products for men, and household and home scented products such as candles, room sprays, potpourris etc which we call ***'anciliary'*** products. Whichever is your preference, indulge in the wonderful world of scent.

There is a reason why there are so many quotes about ***STOP AND SMELL THE ROSES***

"Don't Hurry
Don't worry
You're only here for a short visit
So don't forget to
Stop and Smell the Roses!"
—Walter Hagen

"The Beauty of Life is in each precious moment! Stop and smell the roses." —Unknown

A fragrance has an anatomy, just like us!

Have you ever thought what goes into creating a perfume? Perhaps you had a chemistry set as a kid or even tried to mix your own essential oils? You'll see it's not as easy as you think. Perfumery is both an ART and a SCIENCE. Perfumers study for years to learn organic chemistry and how to identify over 200,000 ingredients or more! This is not an easy task and there are less than 1000 perfumers in the world—in fact, there are fewer perfumers in the world than astronauts. Being a ***"nose,"*** as ***"Master Perfumers"*** are called, is a highly complex job and has always had a higher barrier to entry, and even though it is a $40 billion industry, the perfumers are in a highly rarified class of their own.

But to simplify this alchemy, here is an overview about the construction of perfume and why you love some and not others.

Perfume is designed and constructed with a 'beginning, middle and end' and we refer to this as the Fragrance or Olfactory 'pyramid,' which is a theoretical view of the degree of long-lastingness or evaporation. It usually has three different stages of development; ***top notes, heart notes and base notes.***

The ***top notes*** of the pyramid are usually the lighter ingredients which 'flash off' or evaporate the quickest e.g. fresh, volatile sparkling citrus ingredients such as mandarin, lemon, grapefruit, green and ozonic notes are the best examples of this. The top notes entice you, flirt with you, and like a lover who leaves in the middle of the night, are fleeting, and disappear after a short while! Typically, the top notes last the least amount of time, anywhere from 15 minutes to maybe a half hour.

As the fragrance mixes with your body chemistry the **middle notes** emerge and the beautiful effects of the ***heart notes or 'main theme'*** of the fragrance waft up, leaving the biggest impact and consist of a heavenly mixture of florals, fruity and spices. Floral perfumes are highly popular because they last for a longer time, about 3 hours on the skin, and they weave in and out of the floral and oriental (spicy) families. It is called the main them or the heart because that is the most memorable part of a fragrance, and when you recall a fragrance you love, that is the part that comes to mind most often.

The ***base notes*** of the pyramid are where the deeper, darker, more long lasting, woods, ambers, patchouli and musks tend to be. They are there to provide depth throughout the life of the perfume and affix themselves onto the skin and onto the mid notes, therefore also called ***'fixatives'.*** As the fragrance 'dries down' during this last phase, it is caused the '**dry down**' and is caused by the drying and mixing of a fragrance with a person's natural oils. This means that a perfume that smells fantastic on one individual might smell completely different on another. Usually, the dry down is the longest lasting part of a perfume's scent life, sometimes as much as 8 hours or more. As stated earlier, many fragrances today do not last as long as they used to because certain 'long-lasting' ingredients have been banned.

Below is a typical Olfactory Pyramid depicting the Top Notes, Middle or Heart notes, and Bass notes.

When it comes to how fragrance 'performs' on the skin and one's preferences for either the top, middle and base notes, many fragrance lovers have commented that they may love the way a fragrance smells initially, but not the way it dries down. Or conversely, they don't love the top notes, but love the middle notes and dry down, or some version of fragrance 'wear'! Many find it frustrating that the fragrance changes so much as they wear it. My preference is for a fragrance to have the same theme throughout and my suggestions are for perfumers to create more of a **'linear'** formulation, which is what we offer when we create custom fragrances for our clients. The fragrance stays consistent throughout the 'life' of a fragrance and it becomes like a warm snuggly blanket which envelops you and gives you comfort, makes you feel safe, sensual and you become confident in the fact that this perfume is loyal, won't change and will be consistent.

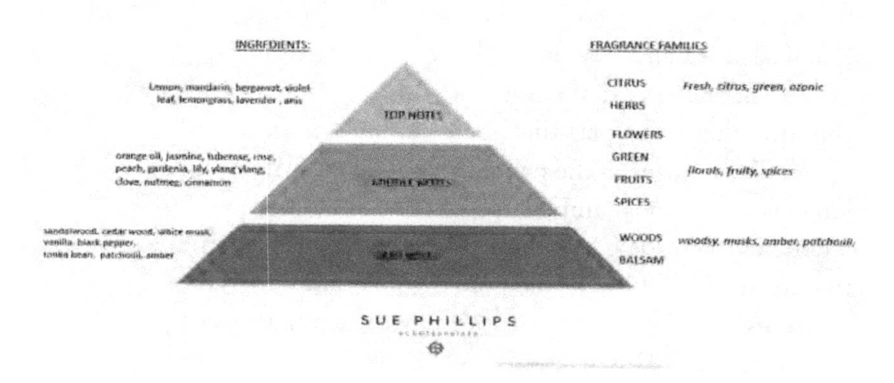

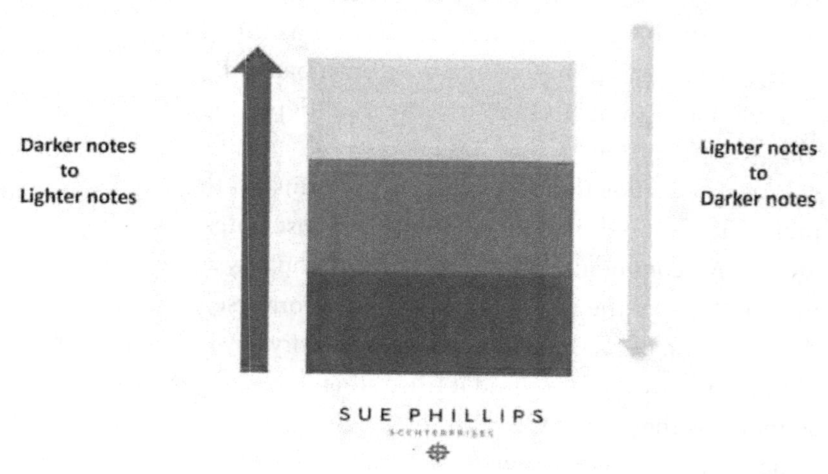

A brief history of perfume

Egypt started it all.

History has shown that the ancient Egyptians loved beautiful fragrances. Like the Cypriots, they associated them with the gods and recognized their positive effect on health and well-being. Perfumes were generally applied as oil-based salves, and there are numerous recipes and depictions of the preparation of perfume in temples all over Egypt.

As sacrifices to the gods, they burned incense and Kyphi (pronounced kee-phee) wood to create a mood and 'sacred' atmosphere for their religious rituals and ceremonies. As the fumes wafted through the air, the word ***perfume*** literally means **'through smoke'** and is derived from the Latin word "per fumus" meaning the very act in which the incense 'fumes' scent the air through smoke. The sweet, pungent aromas wafted through the air, giving the ceremonies a certain reverence and sacredness.

The god of perfume, Nefertum, was also a god of healing who was said to have eased the suffering of the aging sun god Ra with a bouquet of sacred lotus. He could be described as the first aromatherapist!

Egypt was the world leader in the creation of perfume and was closely associated with the international perfume trade. When Julius Caesar took control of Egypt, he demonstrated this fact to the Roman people by throwing bottles of precious perfume to the crowd during his triumphant return to Rome.

The most highly prized perfumes of the ancient world came from Egypt. Of these, arguably the most popular were Susinum (a perfume based on lily, myrrh, cinnamon), Cyprinum (based upon henna, cardamom, cinnamon, myrrh and southernwood) and Mendesian (myrrh and cassia with assorted oils and resins.) Mendesian was named after the ancient city of Mendes, and although the perfume was produced in other locations at a later date, the best variety was still thought to be that from Mendes.

The Egyptians also loved Stakte, a perfume with a fairly strong aroma of Myrrh, Rhondiniu (based on the highly popular scent of rose) and a scent simply known as "the Egyptian" which seems to have been based on cinnamon and myrrh with sweet wine. Perfumes were generally stored in beautiful alabaster bottles, but there is some evidence that blue glass bottles may also have been used.

I recently returned from Morocco and was thrilled to experience the sights, sounds and scents and learned that certain raw materials and ingredients which were used in ancient perfumery are re-surfacing today, as 'scent-designers' and perfumers are re-discovering the past and incorporating fragrant compounds into their modern-day aromatic symphonies. The spice markets are redolent of centuries gone by and literally it was like taking a stroll down the ancient, cobbled streets and stumbling across the spice markets of yesteryear. They are exactly the way they were centuries ago!

Scent Ingredients used in religious rituals.

The ancient Egyptians utilized scents to celebrate prayers and religious ceremony by burning essential oils, resins, and perfumed unguents. According to the Islamic traditions men should use fragrances before prayer. Just like the ritual of washing yourself before prayer, the use of fragrances was seen as an attempt to reach a state of maximum purity in order to build the relation with Allah. To the contrary, from the Middle Ages through the Renaissance, fetid odors were indicative of disease, low social rank, and moral corruption. In the 13th Century, Galbanum was burned in incense holders and used to ward off the evil spirits. Various Spices and Sandalwood were burned by the prophets in their sanctuaries and Buddhists believe that sandalwood increases focus and alertness and encourages meditation.

Perfume links you to Aphrodite, the Greek goddess of Love.

Fragrances have been a luxury for thousands of years, harking back to 2000 BC Cyprus where archeologists unearthed tiny alabaster bottles which had concealed perfumes scented with extracts of lavender, rosemary, pine and coriander, amongst others. In those days these perfumes were linked strongly with the mythological Greek goddess of love, **Aphrodite,** as being a staple of luxury living and love. Aphrodite inspired art, craft and both human and male gods—she was the goddess of beauty and love—so no wonder she is associated with perfume! A 2003 archeological find at Pyrgos on Cyprus, the island where Aphrodite first stepped foot on land after her birth at sea, discovered a perfume-making workshop from circa 1850 B.C., the oldest one in the world. Archeology provides richer information, showing that in ancient Egypt, Palestine, and the Roman Empire, temples almost always had perfume factories nearby producing the great quantities of fragrances they needed.

The Art of Perfumery throughout the Ages.

Following the use of perfume by the Egyptians for their religious ceremonies, other cultures incorporated scented oils, incense and perfumed unguents into their daily rituals for cleanliness and hygiene, and as a symbol of indulgence in the homes of nobility. Queen Cleopatra and Queen Hatshepsut scented their bodies, homes, baths and barges and took perfume with them to the grave. The Greeks, Romans, Mesopotamians and Chinese all used perfumes for their personal use and in religious ceremonies. Noble Chinese began to use personal perfumes, importing ingredients via the Silk Road. By the Yuan, Ming and Qing dynasties, fragrance use had begun to spread among the public. Oriental fragrances focused heavily on herbs and spices, many of which were also used for food and medicine, in their homes and places of worship. The Chinese used perfume for disinfection and purity as they believed that perfume could help rid a room of disease. In general, they focused less on anointing their bodies with fragrance and more on using it to scent the world around them.

The word 'incense' comes from the Latin ***incendere*** 'to burn' and the ancients used aromatic plant materials often combined with essential oils, to release fragrant smoke when burned. In the 14th Century, Galbanum was used in ornate incense holders which were swung back and forth to ward off the evil spirits, and the practice of swinging incense holders continues today in churches.

By the 14th Century AD, Italians had almost perfected the perfume-making process and liquid perfumes began to replace solid ones. Marco Polo brought many unique aromatics back from his travels which turned Venice into a major fragrance trading post. Catherine de Medici is often credited with bringing perfume to the rest of Europe and had her own perfumer, Rene le Florentin, create a signature scent for her out of orange blossom and bergamot.

Perfume started to become a fashion accessory, and European men and women would wear perfume on their bodies, clothing and wigs. People began incorporating more complex ingredients such as ambergris, civet and musk derived from animals. Since bathing regularly was still an unpopular practice, these scents were used to cover up the scent of body odors. The smell of perfume was in vogue because it helped distinguish the upper classes from the stinking masses!

The French perfected it!

Grasse became the Perfume Capital of the World

If you've never been to Grasse, it is a MUST! This little town in the South of France became the center of the perfume industry quite by chance, or perhaps by design! It had the perfect climate, soil and temperature to nurture the growth of all types of fragrant flowers, jasmine, lavender and roses, and with this perfect environment, cattle roamed freely.

In medieval times, the local townsmen realized they needed to harvest both the flowers and the cattle, and they cured and softened the animal hides with chemicals to produce a thriving leather industry. What resulted was the ***Leather Guild of France,*** but they had to find a way to overcome the foul odor and the pungent chemicals and merchandise which wasn't popular with the local nobility. The story unfolds and one of the tanners extracted the oils from the roses, lavender and jasmine which resulted in different technologies called "Enfleurage," "Extraction" and "Distillation"- all methodologies to extract the fragrant oils from flowers. They mixed these with the chemicals to mask the harsh odors from the leather tanning process resulting in supple scented leather which became a perfect ladies' accessory in the form of scented leather gloves. These were presented to Catherine de Medici, who was delighted with her new scented gifts, hence the term *'walking hand in glove"!* Grasse then became known as the ***Perfume Guild of France*** in the 17th Century due to the beautiful flowers growing naturally in the area. Hence, perfume became a very important process as the natural oils were rubbed into the leather to ensure staying power and to overcome the distinctive chemical odor from the leather tanning process. Today Grasse is still known as the perfume capital of the world, and many of today's popular leather perfumes are steeped in the history and origins from that time.

In addition, Grasse' fragrant rose and jasmine flowers that bloom in May are at the heart of many of the world's iconic fragrances, including Chanel No 5. In and around Grasse, major perfume houses such as Dior, Hermès and Chanel all grow roses and jasmine in protected flower fields. Every year the town exuberantly celebrates both of these fragrant blossoms with two festivals, and recently, Dior re-established the famous Château de la Colle Noire, Christian Dior's former residence in Grasse.

On one of my trips to Grasse I spent a wonderful afternoon with legendary perfumer and friend, the chief perfumer of Hermés **Jean-Claude Ellena** and his wife **Susanna**. While talking about perfume I was fascinated to see the exquisite first-edition books of ***'Waiting for Godot'*** on the library shelves. It turned out that Susanna is the great- niece of the writer Samuel Beckett! It is one of my most favorite plays and it was an extraordinary experience to see the signed first edition books! I am continually fascinated how the Arts and Senses are so intertwined.

One of the first modern fragrances by legendary perfumer Francois Coty was ***Chypre de Coty*** a feminine perfume by Coty. The scent was launched in 1917 and the fragrance was created to honor "**Chypre**," in French, which refers to the island of Cyprus, birthplace of Venus, the legendary goddess of love. The name is appropriate because **Chypre de Coty** set the standard for a new type of fragrance, a category which we now refer to as "mossy-woody", which comes from oakmoss, originating from the island of Cyprus, and which was noticeable in the air whenever you visited the island. I had always longed to visit Cyprus and took my daughter Romy there 4 years ago, excited to smell the aromatic 'chypre' in the air. Alas it is a built-up city now, and the tourist stores now only sell little bottles of this elixir as opposed to actually experiencing the natural ingredients wafting in the air, which was the hallmark of Cyprus!

François Coty was not the first to associate the name Chypre with a fragrance, but he innovated it in such a way that led to the creation of a family of fragrances with the same name and creative inspiration that gave birth to many feminine perfumes such as **Mitsouko, Miss Dior, Cabochard, Aromatics Elixir, Givenchy III, Narciso Rodriguez for Her** as well as iconic fragrances for men such as **Aramis, Polo** and **Anteus**. **Chypre de Coty** marks the beginning of the modern era of perfumery. As mentioned earlier, one of the key ingredients of a Chypre perfume is the exotic, smoldering, deep redolent oakmoss, which sadly has to be reconstituted synthetically because of the IFRA regulations, and as a result many of these iconic perfumes do not smell the same.

Guerlain's Chypre de Paris was introduced in 1909. **Chypre d'Orsay** was introduced in 1912, **Molinard's Le Chypre** was introduced in 1925 at a time when Coty's Chypre already had tremendous traction and is generally considered one of François Coty's greatest creations. A true classic! I recently spoke to Veronique Coty, his descendant, who is the President of the Association François Coty in France, and when I asked about him she said, *"Francois died in 1934 and I was born in 1971…I happen to believe in angels and he is my course of action…I talk to him every day and he helps me a lot"*

Fragrance through the Decades

The 1960's began the explosion in the USA

In the 1960s more people began to buy perfume, especially in duty free shops, as travel retail offered a vast array of European perfumes which were previously not as well-known or readily available to Americans. The heady floral ***Madame Rochas*** which was inspired by ***Chanel No 5***, had a modern feel with the addition of Lily of the Valley. The bottle was a replica of an 18th century antique bottle designed by Pierre Dinand, with whom I had the pleasure of working on the Tiffany and Burberry fragrances. The perfume still retains its allure and fascination today as a 'classic.' The era of the 60s was filled with rapid and irrevocable change, causing a new interest in lighter, less cloying scents. As the influence of French perfumery grew, the American Fragrance industry began in the 60's and eventually flourished as a result of more and more American companies entering the category and designers added fragrance to their product portfolio.

The first American designer who was known as "the American Balenciaga" for his couture techniques, refined workmanship and luxurious fabrics was **Norman Norell**, and his perfume ***Norell by Norell*** was launched in 1968 and created by Josephine Catapano. It was created for women but could easily have been for men too as it was a green, woodsy, chypre fragrance and could also be considered unisex in a way.

What would the 60's be without Twiggy? She epitomized that era with her Mini Skirts, and **Musk** and **Patchouli** became very popular as the scents of choice for the hippy generation, since it was thought to deflect the smell of marijuana. Patchouli oil is still a very common base note in perfumes today.

How Perfumes changed in the 1970s.

The 1970s were called the Me Decade. It was a trend-laden, fad-happy decade and people did as they pleased. It was the decade of disco, mood rings, pet rocks, bellbottoms, hip huggers, the leisure suit, platform shoes, designer jeans and the string bikini. While the 60s were full of political and cultural movements, the 1970s shifted away from the social issues and more towards self- examination.

So what did people turn to? The 1970s were full of musky fragrances. It is the decade that saw an increase in unisex fragrances and the creation of the first natural and organic perfumes which were made by **Aveda.**

Fragrance advertising was revolutionized with the launch of ***"Charlie"*** perfume, a peachy, fruity fresh, aldehydic composition, with the Charlie girl striding down the street, defining the decade of the emancipated woman, now seen as a reflection of the working girl. In 1973, now a forgotten drugstore classic, *"CHARLIE"* typified women's 'lib' and women who smoked filter-less Chesterfields. Despite all the other iterations of 'Charlie' flankers from 1973—2000 such as Charlie Blue, Charlie Gold, Charlie Instinct, Charlie Red, Charlie Express, Charlie Silver, Charlie Sunshine, Charlie Urban Energy, Charlie White Musk, only the original *CHARLIE* captivated consumers and alas has gone the way of Where have all the Flowers Gone?

Jovan launched a musk oil which positioned itself as a sex appeal adherent. The success of Charlie and Jovan musk opened the flood-gates to ever more creative and ever more expensive perfume marketing. The perfume gates had opened commercially.

In the early to late 70's, in both America and Europe, fragrance history heralded a new trend—Designers launching their own fragrances—typically modern heady white floral with a hint of green and aldehydic notes. Fragrances from authentic American and European designers such as Norman Norell, Karl Lagerfeld for Chloe, Oscar De La Renta were just a few who launched their eponymous perfumes. **Yves St Laurent** launched **Opium** which was a bold modern oriental spicy concoction with distinctly recognizable cinnamon notes and the name caused a furor! The Chinoiserie-inspired packaging was almost banned by the Chinese Government as they said the drug inference reflected poorly on their culture. The fragrances were feminine, memorable, and had a 'signature'—in other words –they were ***identifiable.*** When one thinks about those perfumes, the notes immediately come to mind and we can go into our memory bank and recall those fragrances as if it were yesterday. Today there are new variations of those classics which are reminiscent of the originals such as the new Chloe, Esprit D'Oscar (The Spirit of Femininity) and Belle D'Opium. In my opinion, however, the originals were iconic and so original and captivating.

The 70's also saw fragrances from other authentic designers from Europe and America, such as **Calvin Klein, Donna Karan, Ralph Lauren, Tommy Hilfiger, Carolina Herrera,** and many others. The designer trend continued throughout the next decade with other milestone 80's moments: sadly, The Beatles broke up in 1970, and it was a decade of 'firsts'**: Diane Von Furstenberg** launched her first wrap dress (true to her philosophy of sexual freedom- it was just as easy to slip out of!); Microsoft was founded, and the first Star Wars premiered!

Perfumes in the 1980s linger on, and on, and on...

The most recognizable fragrance of the 1980's however, was ***Giorgio Beverly Hills*** which was big, bold, decadent, flamboyant, reflected wealth, and the opulent, luxurious lifestyle of Hollywood and Beverly Hills. It became the biggest designer fragrance of the 80s, and it was the fragrance for those with a luxurious mindset and personified the popular TV show ***"Dynasty,"*** with big hair, big shoulder pads, gorgeous clothes and bitchy beautiful, sexy women. It was designed on the supposition that everyone wanted that movie star sort of lifestyle. The perfume was so powerful and recognizable with a strong sweet pineapple floral fruity note and 'sillage' and it was only available at the one and only Giorgio retail boutique in Beverly Hills. However, the brilliance of the marketing was that it was advertised through a scented direct mail postcard and in magazines with a scent-strip, which made it available to everyone to order. And thus, became the start of the ubiquitous 'scent-strip' ads in magazines throughout the country—sometimes as many as 10 in a single issue. The scent was unique, strong, made a killer impression, and was so recognizable, that some restaurants asked that women *refrain* from wearing it, and even printed the request on the menus.

There were other powerful perfumes at that time: ***Poison*** by Dior was distinctive, provocative and sexy with a strong blackcurrant fruity, honey and amber accords. ***Obsession*** by Calvin Klein was overstated and androgynous, with deep sensual oriental amber musky notes and marketed in the hopes of achieving overstated wealth and sex. Subtlety disappeared completely.

And for Men? There's nothing like a good 80's throwback. **Stetson** (smells like sweet alcohol) and **BRUT** (for men) were the colognes-du-jour at that time, proving some brands never die.

Celebrities enter the world of Fragrance

The first Celebrity fragrance **Elizabeth Taylor's *"Passion"*** was launched in 1987 by **Chesebrough-Ponds** Inc which went on to become a spectacular seller, and one of the most successful brands in **fragrance** history. It is still generating millions of dollars annually, and a slew of other fragrances by Elizabeth Taylor were launched.

"***White Diamonds"*** launched in 1991 and was one of the most successful franchises of all time with over $1.5 billion dollars in sales and counting. While Elizabeth Taylor wasn't the first celebrity to come out with a scent, she was the first to do it well. After 30 years, it's still the best-selling celebrity fragrance in the world, bringing in over $200 million globally and according to Forbes generated $20million annually in royalties in 2015 for her estate. That number includes all the fragrances under the Elizabeth Taylor name, including **Black Pearl** and **Passion.** White Diamonds is still the best in the fragrance portfolio and still sees strong sales now that she has passed away, as consumers want to capture a 'piece' of her.

Rhapsody in Blue—Tiffany—an iconic American brand

Of particular importance to me, was the introduction of the iconic, exquisite **TIFFANY** perfume launched by the fine jewelry company **Tiffany & Company** in 1987. I am honored that I was hired to spearhead the creation and development of the first **Tiffany Perfume** as **VP Tiffany, Fragrance Division**, and it was a labor of love. We won a Fifi Award (Fragrance Foundation Award) for the best fragrance introduction.

Developing and launching a fragrance is a very costly and time-consuming undertaking and for an iconic brand such as Tiffany, all the elements had to reflect the ethos of the brand. I was thrilled and honored to go to Paris regularly to collaborate with **Jacques Polge, chief perfumer** of **Chanel**.

So, a word about **Jacques Polge**. He created an elegant and luxurious perfume for women, it was a gorgeous blend of jasmine, orange blossom, iris and rose. It reflected the quality, elegance, richness and sophistication that the Tiffany consumer aspires to own. We followed it up with the successful **Tiffany for Men**, and my suggestion to Jacques was to explore creating the men's formula in the genre of a sensual, masculine, oriental family, rather than the typical light American 'sporty' fragrance. Tiffany eventually licensed the fragrances to Coty, and interestingly I get requests all the time from consumers who would love to purchase the original Tiffany fragrances. In 2021 **LVMH** Moët Hennessy **Louis Vuitton** SE, completed the acquisition of **Tiffany & Co.**

To celebrate the successful perfume launch and to show appreciation to all involved I created a 'rare' memorable gift of a 1oz perfume bottle with a diamond over the "I" (with help from the Diamond Dept) and presented it to management of both companies. Each one was packaged in the Tiffany Blue box, with our names engraved on the bottom of the bottle, and gifted to **Bill Chaney** Chairman of Tiffany & Co., **Alain Wertheimer** Owner of Chanel, **Arie Kopelman** President of Chanel; **Jacques Polge** Chief Perfumer of Chanel, **Suzanne McMillan** VP Tiffany & Co. **Anthony Schepis** VP Manufacturing **Chane**l and one for me! It is a lovely memento of a glorious perfume and the unforgettable 'Rhapsody in Blue" Ad campaign. I still have it, and now and again I see Bill Chaney who lives in my apartment building. I wonder if he still has it?

The 90's become lighter, watery, transparent and unisex

The 90's saw a new trend which came as a reversal and a backlash to the opulent, over-the-top 1980's. This became the time of minimalism, transparency, with conspicuous excesses outmoded. The perfume was light and transparent, and Issey Miyake's ***"L'eau d'Issey"*** appealed to both men and women, and changed the direction from heavy, heady big florals to lighter ozonic, fresh, aquatic, marine notes—described as "fresh and clean" and still very popular today.

Reflecting the denunciation of consumerism and a global recession, **CK One,** as an example, telegraphed that one secretly longed to be part of the goth or at least stoner crowd but wasn't ready for it. Instead, one wore this unisex perfume. **Gap Dream** epitomized one who played soccer, wore a hemp necklace and were a touch unavailable. As women gained entry into the workforce, **Clinique Happy** was for those people who became lawyers but might really want to be a mom. **Drakkar Noir** reflected one who was obsessed with one's best friend's older brother and solaced oneself by spraying it on one's pillow. **Tommy Girl** was for serious girls with a playful personality, longing to fit in.

One iconic fragrance of the 90's decade was **Angel by Thierry Mugler**—the first "edible gourmand' scent, which reflected Mugler's childhood memories: chocolate, caramel, candy floss, and his mother's nail polish remover! A sweet, heavenly, concoction, the marketing embodied the celestial, glamorous sweet yet devilish woman and the bottle was shaped in a 5 point star, and was too beautiful to discard as it was marketed as a piece of sculpture. The interactive 'refilling' or 'dramming' was a terrific in-store event as consumers were able to refill their perfume bottles at less than the price of a new bottle, and were also doing their part to 'recycle.'

2000's Celebrity Fragrances continue to launch

After the successful introduction of Elizabeth Taylor's perfumes, the celebrity fragrance category proliferated! The 2000's saw the rise of **Celebrity Fragrances**, with almost every celebrity launching fragrances, sometimes as many as two a year. The most popular and enduring is still **Jennifer Lopez** with her **GLOW** fragrance since its launch in 2002 and **PROMISE** being the 25th addition to her $2billion franchise.

Can you name them all?

And then there's Paris—of Hilton fame.

Paris Hilton has been in the beauty industry since 2004, when she launched her first fragrance. Since then, her brand is estimated to have done $2.5 billion in fragrance sales. Her most recent fragrance called **Electrify** is meant to capture the ***rush*** Hilton feels when she is DJ'ing. "Electrify was inspired by nightlife, me DJ'ing, and just being on stage and performing in front of people and that amazing feeling I get where I feel like I'm electrified," Hilton said *"When I was a little girl, I always thought I would have one perfume. I had no idea I would have 25 one day."*[7]

---

7 WWD September 30, 2019

Just because you're a celebrity doesn't meant that the cash registers will ring:

Celebrity fragrances are not going anywhere, simply because people still, and will always love them More so, they're great for the celebrity they're attached to because it's an easy way for them to remain visible and relevant during their off-season, and have something to post on their social media channels. However, sales of celebrity scents have dropped by half since 2015[8] while luxury perfumes have seen a recent sales increase of 16 percent, bringing them to a record high. So maybe the tide has turned on celebs hawking juice with their names and faces on them.

To maintain the success of the brand it's important that the celebrity get behind their product and take ownership of it. Even though a celebrity licenses his or her name for a fragrance, it doesn't guarantee success at the cash register, if the fragrance is not supported or truly believed in by the Celebrity. Sadly, in the 2000's, many celebrities jumped on the fragrance bandwagon as it was an easy 'cash cow' for them, but in many instances, the fràgrances were short lived and inauthentic.

You would think that **Lady Gaga and Madonna** would have successful perfume brands. Think again! Both mega superstars introduced their fragrances in 2012, and despite their fame, neither were the commercial successes that they had been projected to be, and actually landed up on clearance at Macy's Department stores (fragrances are NEVER discounted at stores!).[9]

Surprisingly, in a 'whisper' campaign, in 2015 Lady Gaga introduced yet another fragrance **Eau de Gaga,** which had a minimal shelf life.

8 http://wapo.st/3c8sXGE https://www.washingtonpost.com/ modern-life-smells-so-good

9 https://www.fragrantica.com/board/viewtopic.php?id=56552

We are living through a scentual explosion.

As the end of the 20th Century approached, the fragrance world changed yet again. It all started at the time of the millennium in 2000. People became nostalgic for the 'good old days' and therefore all the classic fragrances re-emerged as popular, 'safe' choices for Christmas gifts: **Chanel, Arpège, Shalimar, Guerlain, Dior** offered classic 'safe' staples. This new decade also saw a slew of Celebrity Fragrances being launched, which, based on the success of the Elizabeth Taylor fragrance franchise, became an easy way for celebrities to license their name and pocket whopping royalties from sales. All they had to do was show up for in-store appearances, sign a few autographs, hold interviews and press conferences and show that they were authentically behind their brands, and all the fragrance public wanted was a 'piece' of their favorite celeb and to identify with them. Authenticity was important to the fragrance public, as both A'-list and B-list celebrities all launched fragrances including **Taylor Swift, Selena Gomez, Lady Gaga, Madonna, Britney Spears, Sean John, Rihanna, Beyoncé, Jay-Z, Maria Carey, Jennifer Lopez, Justin Bieber, 50 Cent, Kim Kardashian, Nicky Minaj, Eva Longoria, Ariana Grande, Adam Levine, One Direction and Nicole Richie.** What started out as very lucrative, became overproliferated, and by 2018 the celebrity category had become dismally oversaturated. Interestingly, **Jennifer Lopez** and **Paris Hilton** both launched their 25th fragrances in 2019/2020 and have generated sales in the $2billion stratosphere as they continue to support their brands.

Don't forget the Man in your life! Remember Old Spice?

One of the most iconic Men's Colognes was **Old Spice.** Founded by William Lightfoot Schultz's soap and toiletries company, Shulton Inc., in 1937. It was first targeted to women, under the name ***"Early American Old Spice and*** was inspired by his mother's Potpourri recipe. It flopped, so he came out with the new "**Old Spice**" for men released before Christmas at the end of 1937. This new fragrance became *heavily* intertwined with the US military through WWII, especially in the Navy. The name itself is a reference to "old world spices" used by sailors returning from sea. A certain "smells like the good ol' days" appeal.

My dad wore this, as did many other men, and it was an oriental spicy fragrance and one of the first American brands of male grooming products with deodorants, antiperspirants, shampoos, body washes, and soaps. It is manufactured by Procter & Gamble. The nose behind this fragrance was Albert Hauck. It is a complex fragrance with top notes of nutmeg, lemon, orange, star anise and aldehydes, Middle notes are carnation, jasmine, geranium cinnamon, heliotrope and pimento, and the base notes are ambergris, benzoin, cedar, vanilla, tonka bean and musk. It has been relaunched a few times with new advertising campaigns. It was truly an extraordinary fragrance and I believe the fragrance would still be popular today if rebranded under a totally different name.

In early 2008, the original Old Spice scent was repackaged as "Classic Scent," both in the after shave and cologne versions. The white glass bottles gave way to plastic, and the gray stoppers to red. Old Spice Classic shower gel was sold using the slogan *"The original. If your grandfather hadn't worn it, you wouldn't exist."* In January 2016, Procter & Gamble changed the scent of its Old Spice Classic After Shave. According to the product's website, under ratings & reviews, the change was made in order to "comply with new regulations." This probably means many of the ingredients were either unavailable, too expensive, and they reformulated it with less expensive ingredients!

Marketing is effective to Men for their Grooming Rituals

The ritual of men shaving then slapping their face when applying After Shave lotion was one I remember my dad doing with his Old Spice. Why? Aftershave used to be an antiseptic. It always contained alcohol (ouch) or witch hazel to prevent those occasional nicks and cuts from getting infected. And to stop the burning sensation the men would slap their cheeks with After Shave which was followed by Cologne. In the mid to late 70s, when the perfume craze was happening for women, Companies marketed fragrances and grooming products to men to generate additional revenue. So, After Shave was marketed as an astringent and antiseptic, and Cologne was to be worn as a fragrance after shaving—a matching scent which was invigorating, bracing and scented with a matching grooming product.

With the celebrity perfume craze in the 1990s and early 2000s, male celebrities released colognes (not perfumes). The trend over the past few years was first the Designers launched fragrances, then the Celebrities, and suddenly every celebrity had a fragrance. Companies started to launch Grooming Essentials for Men, with deodorants, gels, moisturizers, After Shaves and men were able to enjoy an entire grooming regimen with the fragrance they enjoyed.

Perfume, meanwhile, was marketed by female celebrities, and the only difference between the two kinds of fragrances were the amount of essential oil they contained, with men's fragrances formulated with citrusy, woodsier and deeper ingredients whereas women's perfumes were floral and a little sweeter.

Niche 'perfumeurs' are the new celebrities

Remember these iconic names? **Elizabeth Arden, Helena Rubinstein, Estee Lauder, Charles Revson**? Those were the 'perfumers' of yesteryear, and they shaped the multi-million-dollar Fragrance Industry, which continues to grow. However, there is a new influx of fragrance movers and shakers whom we are designating as **NICHE PERFUMEURS**—not as big as the big brands, but influential nevertheless, and in most cases are being acquired by conglomerates like **Lauder, L'Oreal, LVMH.**

The new 'perfumeurs' or perfumers are changing the fragrance landscape by using higher quality ingredients—perfumers like **Frederic Malle, Francis Kurdjikian, Killian, Christophe Laudamiel**, who are finding more and more creative ways to combine natural ingredients to come up with unexpected scents that are distinctive. In the old days, you had to be a chief perfumer of a Couturier house. Now the big houses don't need to have a chief perfumer, they can acquire smaller perfumers who are attracting attention and appealing to millennials because they are creating fragrances in a way that are unexpected, that mix and match fragrances into new combinations of scents, and ever expanding ingredients with ouds, tobacco and leather.

Sadly, however, one of the distinguishing attributes that attracted the large companies to these niche perfumers was their creativity and delivering a "WOW!" factor that caused them to be noticed initially, and once acquired, these small brands fall prey to the vicissitudes of corporate bottom-line budgets, and in many instances many of the formulas have been changed, become more commercial, and are not as cutting-edge, daring or as fabulous as they once were.

The High Priestess of the Fragrance World.

Any book about fragrance in the USA would be remiss not to mention and pay homage to **Annette Green** who was known as the ***"High Priestess of the Fragrance World."*** She literally pioneered the Fragrance Industry and established the Fragrance Foundation where she worked for more than 40 years.

In an article in The New Yorker[10], the author Rachel Syne mentions that in a Talk of the Town piece, from 1994[11], about "aromachology," the study of smell's influence on human behavior, Green predicted that someday public spaces would feature "sensory- fulfillment centers," where people could go for an olfactory boost. She certainly was prescient, as that is exactly what has happened in the areas of hospitality, gaming, and retail, where consumers enjoy a *sensory experience* as they identify the signature scent with the properties and return again and again. The properties realize that by offering a positive scent experience it encourages their clients to return and therefore they reap a healthy return on their investment.

---

10 https://www.newyorker.com/culture/on-and-off-the-avenue
/the-grande-dame-of-the-perfume-industry-turns-ninety-five

11 https://www.newyorker.com/magazine/1994/03/07/aromachology-an-extract

In addition, Annette coined a few other phrases such as a "fragrance wardrobe," a collection of perfumes to be worn in rotation according to the occasion or one's mood. Thanks to Annette for being the guiding light and ambassador to the Fragrance Industry

It's all about the ingredients

Naturals & Synthetics

Consumers are becoming more interested in knowing which ingredients they prefer in their fragrances and are constantly researching on the internet. They want to know the details, the strengths, and weaknesses of the ingredients, whether they are organic, natural, or synthetic, while still wanting to be transported by a heavenly aroma.

With all the niche fragrances being created, perfumes are formulated with single note ingredients like OUD leading the way. ROSE is also making a return, not your grandmother's Rose, but a more modern exotic direction.

The cost of essential oils from natural ingredients is a huge factor in the art of perfumery. Pricey ingredients such as Bulgarian Rose Oil which accounts for about 70% of the world's rose oil, takes about 10,000 pounds of rose petals to distill one pound of the highly coveted rose oil. Because of the high price of rose oil, some rose producers 'skirt' the system by diluting the oil with geranium or other essential oils, which contain the same chemical as rose oil. Some of these so-called "rose oils" are 90% geranium to 10% rose fragrances. As a result of the expense, perfumers create a synthetic version which is much less expensive. If there are droughts or floods, the production of natural ingredients is compromised and therefore identical molecules are created to replicate the original formulas—sometimes with success, other times noticeably different.

Oud (pronounced OODH) from the Agar tree is grown in Morocco and is exorbitant as the wood has to become infected with a type of mold which causes the wood to produce oud, a dark, extremely fragrant resin. Apparently, only 2 percent of agar trees produce oud, making it incredibly rare and expensive. It is difficult to harvest, and oud oil is sometimes referred to as 'liquid gold". So perfumers formulate synthetic scent molecules and combine them with traditional essential oils derived from flowers, roots, fruit, woods.

The demand for natural Sandalwood from India and Vanilla from Madagascar is greater than its potential supply and require thousands of pounds to yield a pound of essential oil. If they are not able to harvest these ingredients it impacts production of these precious oils. That is why many perfumes have changed over the years and perfumers replicate the natural ingredients with synthetic molecules.

Consumers have a preference for 'natural' ingredients as it goes along with wanting a healthy life-style, eating organic foods and wearing natural fabrics. While some synthetic ingredients are expensive, ingredient firms are introducing new molecules that are either derived from nature or identical to natural compounds, but many molecules continue to come from petroleum. Naturals is arguably today's biggest trend in ingredients for fine fragrances.

Some reasons why synthetics are used.

Because of exorbitant costs and stringent FDA & IFRA rules prohibiting the use of certain animal products such as ambergris, musk, civet, and castoreum many of these 'ancient' ingredients are manufactured synthetically or 'aromatically.' When you visit a perfume lab you see thousands of bottles, each one containing a mysterious potion that, when combined with others, can create the most extraordinary concoction...which becomes a perfume or fragrance when combined with alcohol.

The derivation of all fragrance ingredients come from nature, and now due to the sophisticated 'head space' technology technique developed in the 1980s, perfumers can analyze the odor compounds present in the air surrounding various objects—such as plants, flowers, foods, and even fabrics. After the data is analyzed, the scents can then be recreated by a perfumer.

Through this technology, Perfumers can pretty much duplicate any aroma! If you ever want to know what the aroma of freshly laundered linen actually smells like, it is possible to find out!

Are Perfumes for Women & Colognes for Men?

Think about this.... Ingredients have no gender! There is no such thing as a masculine lemon or feminine orange! Traditionally, men have preferred woodsier, musky, herbaceous and spicy notes, while women have been known to prefer florals, citrus and amber notes. Marketing campaigns have perpetuated the gender myth ***"........Fragrance for Men"***, or "......***The Perfume for Women***". Generally, European men are comfortable wearing floral fragrances, while American men seem to denounce florals and prefer 'sportier' fresh fragrances. My prediction? The gender syndrome is changing as both men and women recognize which fragrance preferences appeal to them, and in this age of 'selfies,' they become confident in the selection that appeals to them, and not what is marketed to them.

The range of fragrance options has increased greatly as Social media is an important tool for consumers reflecting their own brand. Everyone today has a voice, has their own channel and self-expression is an essential part of today's culture. My male clients say they would like to create their own 'perfume' so more men are requesting "perfumes," not "colognes" and "after shave."

Both Men and Women choose to wear an assortment of scents, for every mood, and occasion to reflect THEIR individuality and personality. They see perfumes as holistic and healing, lifting their moods and even alleviating tiredness or pain. They understand that perfume is a mood changer and choose and create their scents accordingly. What they call this magical elixir is less and less important as long as it gives them that feeling of desirability and confidence!

What connotes the difference in men's and women's fragrances? Can women ONLY wear "women's" fragrances, and the same for men? Absolutely not! In fact, today, men ***actually*** state that they want their own perfume! And many women say they love to wear 'men's' scents—those that are woodsy & spicy.

Marketing to the Sexes[12]

Walk through a department store and you will likely see strict gender-positioned products at various fragrance bars. The colognes are in displays with advertisements of sexy male models or a heterosexual couple in deep embrace, with the cologne itself packaged in a black, grey, dark blue or industrial-looking bottle. Perfumes, meanwhile, are advertised with images of women or a couple that looks loving and sensual, with the perfume itself in more decorative bottles that may be white, clear, red, pink or purple.

That's just perfume marketing for you. But the truth is, cologne isn't necessarily solely for men. The real difference between perfume and cologne is how the fragrances are formulated, and the actual concentration of fragrance oils in the products.

The word perfume is now becoming more generic. I believe that this is a result of this particular generation's obsession with self-expression, and reluctance to care about labels. Consumers are now saying they want to create something that reflects who they are and they don't care to identify with the latest celebrity. People are literally wanting to express who they are.

Many people really think that perfumes are designed only for women. I think the misconception still exists for many as some

12 https://www.mic.com/articles/184778/why-the-idea-that-perfume-is-for-women-and-cologne-is-for-men-is-an-archaic-mindset

products still have 'for men' and 'for women' on their labels for both Eau de Cologne, Eau de Toilette and Eau de Parfum respectively. I believe this is pure marketing and positioned and designed to sell more products. In fact, men can wear perfume and women can wear cologne. It does not inherently make them more attractive or reflect their gender. It's merely a combination of the ingredients which are preferred—more robust, bold and deeper versus the lighter more floral notes, or a combination of both.

Why are there so many 'notes' in this world?

I have always had a fascination for numerology which is "*any belief in the divine or mystical relationship between a number and one or more coinciding events*". It is often associated with astrology and similar divinatory arts. But I think of the Arts when it comes to numerology.

There are 52 keys on the piano which culminates in 8 octaves. Think about Music and the 8 notes in an octave that have produced magnificent sonatas and concertos and the brilliance of the 3 B's **Bach, Beethoven** and **Brahms**, as well as the **Beatles**! and of course all composers too numerous to mention here.

In Art, the 3 primary colors (yellow, blue, red) have yielded magnificent works of arts, which, when mixed and applied in a variety of ways from **Rembrandt,** to **Manet, Monet, Picasso, Pollack, Rauschenberg** and thousands of others, produce truly magnificent works of art.

And what about **Fragrance**? Originally fragrances were harvested from natural ingredients which were used in ancient Egyptian rituals, giving us the very word that means 'perfume'—from the Latin "through smoke". Over the centuries many different natural and more recently[13] synthetic ingredients are used in perfumery giving us **8 different Fragrance Families** which are the framework for glorious perfumes.

There are many different **ingredients** that go into perfume-making and while there is some discourse in the fragrance community over the organization and description of each family, most agree to these 8 following families and subfamilies. Here is a simplified version of the very complex art of perfumery, as this will help you identify which Fragrance Family or Families most appeal to you.

Each of these Families has an array of magnificent ingredients and include both natural and synthetics:

Citrus Family includes lemons, limes, oranges, mandarin, tangerine, grapefruit, bergamot, orange blossoms, petit grain, neroli oil. This falls into the **Fresh** family and Green notes such as 'fresh-cut grass and aquatic or 'ozonic' notes like the smell of the air after a rainstorm. Fresh and Spirited!

Floral Family is the largest family and includes Rose, Gardenia, Jasmine, Tuberose, Violet, Lilies, Frangipani, Cyclamen it expands into Fresh Floral, Light Floral, Fruity Floral, Floriental. Feminine

Fruity Family includes new fruity notes: apricot, raspberry, lychee, apple, melon, raspberry, pineapple, luscious, pomegranate. Luscious and Gourmand

Oriental or Spicy Family also known as "amber" fragrances –vanilla, cinnamon, ginger, incense, food notes chocolate, caramel. Luxurious and exotic often associated with warmth and sensuality.

Chypre (Cyprus)—mossy, leathery, based on oakmoss, patchouli and bergamot -rich, lingering, sexy

---

13 It was not until the late 1800's when synthetic chemicals were used, that perfumes could be mass marketed. The first synthetic perfume was nitrobenzene, made from nitric acid and benzene. This synthetic mixture gave off an almond scent. The most famous synthetic molecule was aldehydic used in Chanel No 5 and discussed previously.

Woodsy—notes of cedarwood, sandalwood, birchwood —natural and the great outdoors

Fougères Aromatic (Fern-like)—herbaceous notes, lavender, sage, coumarin, thyme, rosemary, mint

Animalic—Musk notes—from deer or civet cat; now natural plant musks, amber originally ambergris—deep, sexy, pungent scent

The Fragrance wheel is a classification method that is widely used in retail and in the fragrance industry. The method was created in 1983 by Michael Edwards, who designed his fragrance classification to simplify fragrance families as well as to show the relationships between each individual family. The four standard families consist of *Fresh, Floral, Woody, Oriental* and they can all be intertwined.

The Fragrance Wheel might be somewhat complicated for some people to digest, and so we have narrowed the Fragrance Families even further to 4 MAIN OLFACTORY GROUPS: **Fresh, Floral, Woodsy and Oriental (Spicy**). These represent the four main olfactory groups with each having distinct characteristics. More often than not, a person will gravitate toward one scent family over another and look for this collection of scents in their fragrances. Which family or families appeals to you?

FRESH FAMILY: This family consists of light bright citrusy ingredients s eg. Lemon, lime, orange, tangerine, grapefruit, bergamot, and all the invigorating light, energetic notes. For this family, I also include the breezy watery ozonic scents which have a 'marine' note, as well as 'green' notes such as fresh-cut grass and luscious fruity notes including watermelon, berries, melons. These are considered 'TOP NOTES' and loved by men and women and last the shortest time on the skin—for about 15- 20 minutes on the skin and are fleeting. But they 'draw' you in with their vibrant and spirited and refreshing notes and are like a lovely Spring Day.

FLORAL FAMILY: As its name implies it includes all the magnificent florals e.g. Rose, Jasmine, Lily of the Valley, Gardenia, Frangipani, Cyclamen, Violet Leaf, and can be soft and subtle, or bold. In addition, it can also expand to include fresh floral, light floral, fruity floral and flora-oriental fragrances which we call floriental. As you would agree this category largely appeals to women, but in my experience European men happen to love florals and do not mind admitting that. They are a little more secure in their 'masculinity' and appreciate the category for the beauty of the ingredients, rather than categorizing them as 'women's ingredients'. There is no such thing as masculine or feminine ingredients. It is how the fragrance is marketed that categorizes them as 'For Women" (usually florals) and "For Men" (usually woodsy, spicy and fresh! Floral notes are mostly the MAIN THEME, MIDDLE NOTES or "heart" of the fragrance and may last about 3—4 hours on the skin, depending on the concentration : whether it be a Perfume, Eau de Parfum, or Eau de Toilette.

WOODSY FAMILY. This family includes all the sensual ingredients from the great outdoors and forests. Notes of cedarwood, sandalwood, birchwood, and I also include the Herbaceous notes such as Lavender, Rosemary, Thyme and the deep, dark, sensuous Chypre notes of patchouli, leather, oakmoss which are sophisticated and comforting. These are considered BASE NOTES which are the longest lasting and may last as long as 5—6 or more hours on the skin. As mentioned earlier, certain ingredients are now disallowed by the regulatory bodies as they are considered 'allergens' and so these long-lasting natural ingredients such as Oakmoss are no longer allowed to be used and so they are formulated synthetically and don't last as long these days.

ORIENTAL—SPICY FAMILY A shy retiring person would not wear this family of fragrances. It is all about sensuality, excitement and a flair for the exotic. Incense, vanilla and musk are used in this category as well as delicious food notes of chocolate, caramel, and all the ingredients in your spice cabinet—ginger, cinnamon, black pepper. These ingredients can also be formulated with florals for the Main

Theme or Middle Notes as florientals, or with the Woodsy family to make the fragrance base notes exotic and bold. This family also can last for about 5-6 hours depending on the concentration.

"If perfume be the food of love, dab on!"[14]

In the same way that Shakespeare heralded the glory and wonder of music by comparing it to food and drastic consequences would ensue if one overindulged, Perfume instills an enormous amount of pleasure & joy.... and it has been known to induce healing! Many ingredients that were used in ancient perfumery introduced a healing element or remedy, and today many of those ingredients are still used in modern fragrance-making.

The definition of the words "**Perfume,**" "**Fragrance,**" "**Aroma**" **or "Scent"** all have one attribute in common, and that is that perfume is a substance, extract or preparation for diffusing or imparting an *agreeable or attractive* smell; a sweet or pleasing scent, and it refers to perfume, cologne and toilet water. Aroma is an odor arising from spices, plants, cooking, etc., especially an *agreeable* odor or fragrance.

AROMATHERAPY VS AROMACHOLOGY—what's the difference?

In many instances, Aromatherapy and Aromachology are linked to perfumery and in much the same way that today's blended families

14 * Duke Orsino: If music be the food of love, play on, Give me excess of it; that surfeiting, The appetite may sicken, and so die. *Twelfth Night* Act 1, scene 1, 1–3 by WilliamShakespeare

are related, so are these. Studies have shown, as an example, that peppermint oil will make you more alert, lavender will relax you, citrus will energize you. Healers throughout the millenia and to this day are using herbs such as calendula and marigolds to heal moods and skin diseases. ***Robert Tisserand*** started the whole flower therapy, making them into essential oils which are used to heal depression, shyness, fear and other emotions simply by smelling the flower oils, leading to the notion that **Aromatherapy has proven to be essential healing.**

I still don't think people understand the difference. Our forefathers and mystics used herbs, roots, flowers and woods to create unguents to create healing remedies.

Aromatherapy is a form of alternative medicine, and has its origins in antiquity with the use of infused aromatic or fragrant essential oils extracted from plants, as a treatment to relieve tension and cure certain minor ailments for the purpose of altering a person's mind, mood, or health. ***Aromatherapy*** has been 'pooh-poohed' as "folk science" regarding how scents can be used to heal. In Science, aromatherapy is not yet considered scientifically supported...in fact, it has been purported to be "junk science"—but it has a huge "junky" following! Aromatherapy only uses natural fragrances, not artificial ones, while aromachology advocates the use of both.

Aromachology is the scientific study of olfactory effects in humans. If you want to talk about the science of smell, you should use the term "aromachology" to really show that you're talking about science. While it's easy to get confused between the two, there are some clear differences:

While aromatherapy can be used to treat conditions related to mood and emotion—through inhalation or burning of scents, it's not the primary purpose of aromatherapy. However, influencing moods and emotions is central to aromachology.

While the two have differences, they do complement each other. In fact, the science behind aromachology has validated many historic aromatherapy claims. For example, thanks to aromachology's scientific studies it's been proven that Rosemary enhances cognitive performance, Peppermint is invigorating and Lavender is relaxing.

While aromachology looks at ***why and how*** scents trigger a psychological response in humans, aromatherapy looks at ***which scents cause a specific physiological response***. Aromatherapy is also about healing, while aromachology is often used for commercial purposes, for example in shops to encourage shoppers to spend. **Aromachology** is a fairly new term, coined in 1989 by the Fragrance Foundation, and is the study of the influence of odors on human behavior and examines the relationship between feelings and emotions such as relaxation, exhilaration, sensuality, happiness and well-being brought about by odors stimulating the olfactory pathways in the brain and, in particular, the limbic system.

Fragrance has always been a combination of Science and Art but in ancient times perfume oils were used for anointing, perfuming, lubricating, illuminating and heating. "Health and Wellness" is a term currently used today for ingredients that promote wellbeing. In ancient times the act of applying sacred aromatic oils to the priests' robes, articles of furniture, and to their utensils was a way in which the act of anointing consecrated them to divine service, hence their holiness was contagious.

Many Ancient precious oil ingredients are still used.

Many precious oils used in perfumery in ancient times are now being added in modern perfume labs even though the rationale for using them may have changed. The actual aromas or scents in some cases are so diffusive and 'agreeable' that in many instances certain fragrance oils used in modern perfumery have the added value of not only smelling quite wonderful, but promoting wellness as well.

Galbanum is a gum resin extracted from a plant that grows in Persia (now Iran) and is one of the oldest to be used. At first it emits a disagreeable odor when burned, but when it is blended with the other aromatics, it has the effect of making it pungent and fresh. The earthy and woody aroma of this oil brings pleasure to mind and soul. In the Book of Exodus 30:34 it is mentioned as being used in the making of a perfume for the tabernacle. In the 1100s galbanum was included in the rituals with incense as a reminder to unrepentant sinners to come back to the church and to repent!

The health benefits of Galbanum essential oil can be attributed to its properties like anti-arthritic and anti-rheumatic remedies. Wellness indeed! Today, Galbanum is used in many perfumes such as Chanel

19, Must de Cartier, Vent Vert by Balmain, and Cabochard by Madame Grés. It has a leafy green note and is used in Fougére and Chypre perfumes (Green, Ferny shrubs and leaves from Cyprus).

Galbanum is lovely in combination with Hyacinth and also with florals. It gives a natural green feeling to perfumes and is perfect in oriental fragrances as well. because of the warm green scent that combines with rich balsamic notes.

As we know, Frankincense (also known as Olibanum), and Myrrh were referred to in the bible, and are gum resins which were extracted from trees that are native to Southern Arabia and Northern Somalia. They were used in aromatic anointing Oils. Solidified Myrrh exudes from the ducts of the trunk, and branches of trees, and flows freely if one makes a cut in the bark, and it hardens when exposed to air. The scent of raw myrrh resin and its essential oil is sharp, pleasant, somewhat bitter. The scent is used in mixtures of incense, to provide an earthy element to the overall smell, and as an additive to wine.

The Egyptians believed in its healing powers and they burned Myrrh every day as part of their worshipping rituals. In the Greek culture when soldiers went to battle it was an essential part of their combat gear because of myrrh's extremely high antiseptic and anti-inflammatory properties. It was used to clean wounds and to prevent infection.

Spices and perfumes were rare in the ancient world and very costly because of the huge amounts of raw materials needed to manufacture the desired quantity, and the great distances to transport them by land caravan or by sea. The highly specialized aromas of perfumery required an exceptional level of skill and experience.

Why does everyone love Vanilla?

One of the most universally popular ingredients found in perfumery is Vanilla which reminds us of our childhood and conjures up our most pleasant memories. Vanilla is Spanish for 'little pod' and the second most expensive spice after saffron, because growing the vanilla seed pod is labor-intensive.

Despite the expense, vanilla is highly valued for its flavor which is pure, spicy and delicate. As a result, vanilla is widely used in both commercial and domestic baking, perfume and aromatherapy. It is the main note in many of the world's most popular and successful Oriental fragrances, which are a combination of ancient and modern ingredients such as: vanilla, balsamic resins like Olibanum, Balsam tolu (a resin balsam from Peru) and musk. They have been described as Sweet, Spicy, Fruity and Animalic.

One of the most famous fragrances in the world is the beautiful oriental perfume called **"Shalimar"** by Guerlain. It has a foundation of vanilla, topped off with bergamot and citrus notes with other trace ingredients, but the signature, however, is the beautiful and extremely long lasting, diffusive vanilla character. Thierry Mugler's **"Angel"** perfume is also based on a distinctive vanilla gourmand note and is constantly ranked in the top ten fragrances world-wide.

Despite the fact that the use of aromatherapy in treating medical conditions remains scant, there is some evidence that essential oils may have therapeutic potential. Who would ever think that the wrinkled and crinkled Vanilla bean is one of the world's most sought-after ingredients that offers pleasure and wellbeing? Think about the joy and happiness that a vanilla ice-cream gives a child, and how the aroma of freshly baked vanilla cookies welcomes a new neighbor.

Indeed, if music (and perfume) be the food of love, play on!

Perfume is about Romance, Sex, Sensuality

We know that Sex sells, right?

SEXUAL ATTRACTION is one of the strongest factors that influences our choice of fragrances. e.g. ***"Will this fragrance make me more attractive to the opposite sex?"***

Have you ever been attracted to someone and then when you come close you are turned off?

It happened to me. True! I had a crush on someone for a long time, and when we finally got together, phew! What a turnoff! I ran!

What is it about body chemistry that appeals to some and repels others? Is it cultural, gender-specific or demographic? We don't exactly know how or why perfume molecules react with the skin differently on every person, but BODY CHEMISTRY goes a lot deeper that just affecting the way a perfume smells on you. How your mate smells can have a huge impact on ***you***! It's a phenomenon called ***body-odor attraction.*** Why in Europe is the smell of undeodorized, unshaved underarms so appealing, and in the USA and UK a total turnoff? Why do Americans want to smell "Fresh and Clean"? and Europeans are ok with smelling "musky"?

Why do animals have such an acute sense of smell? They can detect water moisture with their noses or smells under the soil. Some even have a sense of smell so sharp it's possible for them to detect smells over vast distances. Sniffer or Detection dogs are trained to detect substances such as explosives, illegal drugs and contraband electronics such as illicit mobile phones.

Human beings don't have a functioning 'vomeronasal' organ which is what other animals use to detect pheromones secreted by another animal of the same species. Instead, we sense smells via the olfactory system. Perceivable smells likely do play a role in attraction, or lack of attraction, in people.

So, while some in-heat animals lift their tail and toot out some horny pheromonal signals, we have evolved slightly differently.

Are our signals today Tinder, Grindr, and Instagram? Well then, it's got to be something else, if not pheromones. Here's some truth about B.O. and attraction, says Lindsey Bordone, assistant professor of dermatology at Columbia University Medical Center, *"Perceivable smells likely do play a role in attraction, or lack of attraction, in people." It's not the* odor *you're actually attracted to. You might just be more forgiving of it because you're attracted to the other person and the overall, underlying scent that is uniquely theirs.*

"The favorable smells that make up a person's scent are more a combination of their body wash, shampoo, deodorant, fragrance, hair product, fabric-softener sheets, and other scented products used throughout everyday life. While there is uniqueness to a person's scent, there are many other things that influence the final 'product'." This is why you might instantly associate someone with the smell of their fragrance that lingers when you kiss, or the inimitable blend of fresh products that trails him or her.

Ever wonder why people are so affected by perfume?[15]

There are two theories that explain how and why fragrance affects our behavior[16]—one which actually affects our bodies like a drug, to produce change e.g. Peppermint and Citrus boosts productivity; the other is that aromas take on the properties of the associated emotions and how it affects our experience and learning. There is credible evidence that odors can affect mood, physiology and behavior, and so during an event that is emotionally charged, what you smell at that moment becomes indelibly tattooed on your brain and intimately intertwined with the experience. Think about an old flame and the fragrance he wore….If you were treated well, every time you smell the fragrance you associate it positively and like it; and vice versa if he treated you badly… even the most commercially successful fragrance will cause you a headache if you associate it negatively!

There are scientific terms for this[17]:

---

15 Aromatherapy Facts and Fictions: A Scientific Analysis of Olfactory effects on Mood, Physiology & Behavior Rachel Herz https://bit.ly/30NeVnF

16 https://www.ncbi.nlm.nih.gov/pmc/articles/PMC5198031/ Influence of Fragrances on Human Psychophysiological Activity by Kandhasamy Sowndhararajan and Songmun Kim*

17 https://www.realmenrealstyle.com/fragrance-theory-affect-behavior/ Real Men Real Style

The Pharmacological Hypothesis: This posits that fragrances affect our systems directly by:

Acting on our bodies like drugs. They enter into our bodies and mess with various hormone levels and neurotransmitters in order to produce change. Some fragrances, like lavender, have been shown to ***directly influence*** certain chemicals in the brain. Studies with rats have shown that if the olfactory system is destroyed, some fragrances still have effects, meaning that fragrance can be absorbed into the body. There is no real proof for this, however.

The Psychological Hypothesis: In this theory, fragrances produce effects through our experience and learning, memories, conscious perceptions, beliefs, and expectations. For instance, the smell of dogs can be quite different for those who had a beloved childhood dog, and those who have been attacked by a dog. Evidence for this theory is that there are direct connections between the effects of smell and the parts of the brain associated with emotions and memories.

The olfactory nerve, which enables us to smell, travels right next to the amygdala and hippocampus, both involved with strong emotions and memories and learning and that is why our Sense of Smell triggers memories and emotions. How many of us remember an experience immediately when you smell a familiar scent —so smells actually ring bells.

Fragrance and Music—a strong sensory relationship

I love to speak and write about the relationship between Music and Fragrance…there is even a similarity in the vocabulary. In my opinion there is a strong sensory relationship between fragrance and music (and even Art), yet people don't really think about that! I believe firmly in the magic and mystery of fragrance as well as in the beauty of music and art! For example: the vocabulary is similar between music and fragrance… we talk about ***notes, harmony, composition, symphony, blends, chords, flats, sharps, and even "dissonance"*** in both. Similarly, the construction of fragrance and music is parallel... both have a beginning, middle and end. Classical music has an *overture, main theme and finale* and Fragrance is constructed with top notes, middle notes (which is the main theme or 'heart' of the fragrance), and ends with deeper base notes, which is the dry down. Art, too, has a foreground, middle ground and background). Both fragrance and music stimulate the senses and trigger memories and emotions.... however, our Sense of Smell is our most powerful and strongest sense after Sight!

I also believe that 'major' and minor' musical chords "color our senses." Think about the fragrance and musical notes which come to mind when we experience bright pinks, sparkling yellows, vibrant reds, mellow blues, bold greens, and luscious rich exotic purples?

They might make you imagine beautiful florals, lively citrus, spicy, gourmand fruity, herbaceous accords which reflect the MAJOR keys and connote "happy, bright, positive" notes. Whereas "MINOR" chords are "sadder" and more subdued and we think of muted deep earth tone colors and fragrance accords of woody, musky, amber, patchouli, mossy fragrance accords.

The idea of correlating and studying the relationship of Music, Fragrance and even Art to stimulate the "Scentsory" palate is a compelling way to produce more interesting, unusual, distinctive approaches with fragrance combinations that stretch the imagination. What would **Stravinsky's "Firebird"** smell like? I see **Vivaldi's "Four Seasons"** spanning four major fragrance families: FRESH, FLORAL, WOODY and SPICY ... And each one is a symphonic and fragrance masterpiece in its own right! Even other musical genres such as hip hop, folk, Latin, pop and rock give perfumers great opportunities to create innovative fragrance "melodies"- something I would love to see more of!

Both music and fragrance don't change your hormone levels, but they DO influence your brain systems involved with perception and memory. The similarities of both music and fragrance can affect one's mood and emotions in the same way. Sometimes you're in the mood for a fast and loud song, sometimes a quiet song. Perhaps a song reminds you of a good (or bad) memory of a person.

Indigenous music and songs speak to your personality or culture. Music stimulates creativity.

Music soothes and inspires, makes you lively and happy.

Synesthesia—do you smell colors and feel sounds?

If you "smell" colors, "feel" sounds, "taste" shapes, you might have synesthesia.

Synesthesia joins objects such as letters, shapes, numbers or people's names with a sensory perception such as **smell, color, sounds or flavor**. It is an extraordinary phenomenon where a sensation in one of the senses, such as hearing, triggers a sensation in another, such as taste. Letter-**color** synesthesia **is** the most common form, where people see letters as having **colors** and they have visual experiences when they smell odors e.g. what does the color red smell like? In a research study at Radboud University in Netherlands, they found that people who see colors while perceiving smells are better at distinguishing between different smells and different colors, and are better at naming odors, compared to a group without synesthesia.

Receiving a compliment makes you feel confident and.... sexy!

When you receive a compliment about how wonderful you smell, it is a game-changer! You suddenly sit or stand up straighter, smile more broadly, and in fact, have an extra spring in your gait! You feel more beautiful, more powerful, more positive, more confident. You become YOU! You exude your feelings in a sensual, subtle way, one that lifts you and those around you. Recent research in neuroscience has shown that receiving a sincere praise activates and releases Dopamine which is associated with motivation, focus, and positivity, the same areas in our brain that are activated when we receive money or romantic attention. In other words, it activates the ***reward circuit in our brain.*** When we receive a compliment for something we have done, it is essentially a signal to our brain saying 'do it again', and you're encouraged to repeat the same task to be able to feel that rewarding 'high' again and again.

By choosing a fragrance that uplifts you, that inspires you, that makes you feel self-assured, you have given yourself 'permission' to feel positive. All of the above communicates your poise and 'confidence' to other people.

Sincerity, however, is the key. When you are complimented on your fragrance by someone you like, admire or love, you will want to wear it again and again. Compliments are wonderful. They are free, easy to offer, and they go a long way in building trust and friendship. So, if you're given a compliment on your fragrance it conveys to you that it suits you and reflects your personality! For as science shows, a little appreciation goes a long way in making people feel and act better. So, praise away, for a better and healthier world!

"LOVE is a perfume you cannot pour onto otherew sithout getting a few drops on yourself." —Ralph Waldo Emerson

Which ingredients make a perfume sexy?

It's never a good idea to generalize but **straight** men seem to prefer a brisk **Eau Sauvage** (Dior) modern bergamot/citrus aromatic scent with a twist of contemporary crowd-pleasing ambroxan (synthetic ambergris), sandalwood and musk to make him feel sexy. The citrus never totally burns off, even in dry-down, but it gradually becomes woodsier, almost leathery (but not quite). This is a true masculine cologne. Straight men still want that citrus 'sporty' scent but are now willing to add a gentle floral ingredient, eg cyclamen and frangipani, which women wear. But they seem to prefer ouds and have traditionally gone for sandalwoods as ouds, vanilla, patchouli, musk are traditional sexy perfumes.

As crazy as this may sound, there is real scientific evidence to suggest that **gay** men are wired to smell differently than their heterosexual counterparts. Swedish scientists found that gay men and straight men responded differently to two odors thought to be involved with sexual arousal[18]. The findings suggested that gay guys respond and are turned on in the same way as women.

---

18 The two chemicals in the study were a testosterone derivative produced in men's sweat and an estrogen-like compound in women's urine, both of which have long been suspected of being pheromones. Nicholas Wade, "For Gay Men, an Attraction to a Different Kind of Scent" (2005) "The New York Times" May 10, 2005; http://www.nytimes.com/2005/05/10/science/10smell.html?ex=1117598400&en=5a3bcc9d4ecaa580&ei=5070&th&emc=th

Gay guys tend to like very sexy pungent scents (aka *body odor*) with musk and many believe that ylang- ylang has an aphrodisiac component to its fragrance. Sexy smells, well, often smell like bodily scents but better. Perhaps one thing that appeals both to some gay men and some women, is the smell of a man's sweaty body. What's the difference between BO and a semi-strong man-scent?

When a guy comes out of a shower, and his body heat gets him all 'steamed' up, and you can see him soaking through his t-shirt, it's extremely erotic And if you are fortunate enough to get a whiff of him, it's like yummy ice cream and marshmallow all rolled up in to one. But as the sweat dries and is absorbed into the fabric, during the day, it can turn into body odor. By 4pm or 5pm it can really become offensive, especially when he removes his jacket. There is science to man-scent. Specifically, it's all about **androstanol**[19]. That's the clinical name for freshly made sweat containing pheromones. And research says it acts as a sexual magnet! Is it any wonder why so many guys get into armpit sniffing? My English grandmother once told me: "Horses sweat, Men perspire, and Ladies gently glow"!

Ambergris or grey amber is a solid, waxy, flammable substance of a dull grey or blackish color produced in the digestive system of sperm whales and accelerated when the bones of the cuttlefish irritates the stomach lining! As a result of the stomach irritation, the sperm whale regurgitates and freshly produced ambergris is washed up on the shore and perfumers, looking for interesting ingredients realized the treasure they had found. It has a sweet, pungent aroma with a marine, fecal odor, and is very expensive, hundreds of thousands of dollars for a pound of ambergris. Regulatory bodies have decreed that animal ingredients such as Ambergris and Musk are no longer to be used in perfumery and therefore synthetic versions are formulated. Perfumeurs of old found this to be an amazing ingredient, but today amber comes from natural plants or synthetics. Close but not like the real thing!

19 Androstenol is the scent produced by fresh male sweat, and is attractive to females. Androstenone is produced by male sweat after exposure to oxygen – i.e. when less fresh – and is perceived as highly unpleasant by females (except during ovulation, when their responses change from 'negative' to 'neutral').

"Home is where the Heart is."

A 'welcoming' home usually has a lovely pleasant aroma wafting in the rooms, whether it be the smell of vanilla & spice cookies; freshly baked bread diffusing from the kitchen; leafy green fronds wafting in the hallway, or a bouquet of flowers in the living room and bedrooms.

The history of Home fragrances, as with perfume, also developed over five thousand years ago in places like Egypt, with aromatic herbs and resins to mask the smell of animal sacrifices, and scents were used in religious ceremonies by the Greeks to communicate with the gods. In the 12th century Galbanum, an aromatic gum resin, with a somewhat musky odor and intense green scent, was used with incense in chalices aka as a 'thurbile' a metal censer suspended from chains, which were swung back and forth (which is still practiced today in the Catholic Church) to ward off evil spirits and as a reminder to unrepentant sinners.

Scent and Medicine have always been linked as scented ingredients were widely used to cover the smell of corruption, body odor, and sickness particularly with the Black Death which ravaged the Middle East, Asia and Europe during the 14th century. Long ago, European physicians believed that "bad air" caused illnesses—scientists like Louis Pasteur, Robert Koch, and Joseph Lister hadn't yet delivered scientific proof of the germ theory of disease. To safeguard themselves against the 'smelly' miasma, as they called this harmful air, doctors donned a curious accessory while treating sickly patients: a mask with a long, 'crow'-like beak, which was stuffed with a range of herbs and spices, dried flowers such as rose petals, mint, cloves, and ambergris, all still popular in modern home fragrance. This costume was worn by the "plague doctor" during the Carnival of Venice, as it is associated with Il Medico della Peste, the famous *commedia dell'arte* character

Romance:

Beware of perfumes men hate[20]

If you're a woman who accessorizes with perfume, consider this: According to men, you might stink! Since Americans spend close to $5 billion on fragrances a year, it's time to make sure we're getting our money's worth. If you're a woman who accessorizes with perfume, consider this:

I was interviewed for an article a few years ago about which women's fragrances appeal to men, and men were asked what they liked and don't like about women's perfumes. Check out their comments and my disclaimers about how things have changed and tips for picking a scent: THEN and NOW.

THEN: Avoid "grandma scents": Certain scents trigger memories, and your scent certainly shouldn't bring up memories of grandma. As eloquently put by one man, *"I hate any pungent smell that, with my eyes closed, makes me feel like I'm hugging my grandmother. It's a concoction somewhere between potpourri and church incense."* Another told us, *"Tea Rose smells like Grandma at a quilting bee. Whenever a younger woman is wearing it, she immediately looks like my Nana to me."*

---

20 https://www.foxnews.com/lifestyle/he-says-you-stink-perfumes-that-men-hate

SP NOW: Tea Rose was launched in 1977 and was hugely popular and VERY rosy! While it might be available today it does not have the appeal that it once had! And as discussed, certain Rose perfumes can remind men of their grannies!

THEN: Flowery perfumes failed the test: Across the board, men were against floral scents. One even said that *"Overly flowery and sweet is a turn off."* A few other men said that floral perfumes remind them of old women (see above). However, the current aversion to flowery perfumes could be due to factors beyond the nose's knowing.

SP NOW: What a difference a few years makes! These days, more and more men do like floral perfumes and realize that they can expand their selection beyond Ouds, Citrus, and Amber scents.

THEN*: Always remember, spritz lightly:* No matter which scent you choose, don't overdo it. According to one guy, there's few things less sexy *"than the overbearing smell of perfume."* No man (or woman) wants to taste your perfume in the air. The safest way to apply perfume is to spray it in front of you, then walk into the mist.

SP NOW: I disagree with the comment to spray perfume in front of you and walk into the mist. That is such a waste of your expensive perfume, and all the scented hair products will distort it too. Perfume should be applied on clean, moisturized (unscented) skin at the 'pulse' points (at the wrists, in the crook of the elbows, in the chest area, at the nape of the neck.

Where to wear a perfume?

The French tell us how to wear a perfume properly.

I am often asked: "How do I wear a fragrance?" On one of my business trips to Paris, I learned the correct way from a perfumer who said to me with a French accent: *"Americans have no idea how to wear ze parfum! In France, we have been wearing parfum for centuries, and we know parfum rises, so we apply it from ze bottom up; at our ankles,* (so zat ze long swishing skirts will make ze fragrance waft up), *behind ze knees, inbetween ze thighs, and at all ze pulse points. You, Americans, just spritz it behind each ear. Who are you attracting… ze birds or ze clouds?"* I always end my seminars this way and people are delighted with the "actress" in me and the actual new-found knowledge of how to apply fragrance.

It goes back to how the French first wore fragrance a century ago.... at a time when bathing and cleanliness were associated with luxury, power, religious purposes, beauty and a ritual of the wealthy or nobility. Strangely enough, although we view bathing as a private matter today, it was a shared ritual for thousands of years—a way to build community and human connection. It was not that popular (nor available) for the masses, and perfume was used to mask body odors. They wore fragrance by dabbing or applying perfume from the bottom up and as Coco Chanel said—*"**Wear perfume wherever you want to be kissed.**"*

The lesson learned is that we know heat rises, that's why doctors take your pulse on the inside wrist, because as your heart pumps blood through your body you can feel a pulsing in some of the blood vessels close to the skin's surface e.g in your wrist, and at the nape of the neck; warmer areas than other areas of the skin. In order to get the best fragrance diffusion results, apply perfume at the pulse points –all 'warmer' areas of the body. Let it envelop you! Men too, should also apply fragrance on the chest, and at the nape of the neck.

Another complaint from clients is that "my fragrance doesn't last"! While perfume is the strongest concentration and most expensive, many people therefore tend to purchase Eau de Parfum or even Eau de Toilette. In addition, fragrances are not as long-lasting as they used to be, and with so many scented bath, body and hair products to choose from, all with conflicting aromas, they will detract from your beautiful expensive perfume, and possibly even undermine it. I recommend using unscented bath products: soap, lotion, deodorant, and then apply your fragrance at the pulse points. This way, YOUR fragrance won't be neutralized. Don't allow an inexpensive, conflicting, possibly synthetic or 'cheap' fragranced soap, or body products to compete with the 'star' performer.

Should perfume be sprayed on clothes? I strongly advise against it. Firstly, certain fabrics are delicate and the perfume oils will stain the clothes. In addition, fabrics don't 'breathe' so if you spray a fragrance on your clothes, it will linger there and the next time you spray a different fragrance on the same fabric, it will distort it.

My advice today is to wear fragrance lavishly on clean, moisturized, unscented skin.

Enjoy it, indulge in it. Spray, dab or splash it all over!

Layering—
A way to wear perfume.

The ability to become your own 'mixologist' is becoming more and more popular, and perfumers and store sales associates will sell you two perfumes so you can combine and wear them together, to create a special scent. These are symphonic ideas, counterpoints such as mixing an amber and oud with a violet rose and ginger. For people who always want to be 'unique' and to have a 'signature' scent, this is the way to create that. Layers of scents. This is for the perfume addicts among us. It is not the traditional way of creating a 'custom' scent, but layering is a great way to discover how different fragrances combine to create an aroma you love. Be aware, however! NOT all fragrances are meant to be mixed. In the same way that you might be tempted to combine different red wines to make your 'own blend' you might land up with a terrible headache instead!

Perfumes are complex; there are a variety of notes to savor.

A beautiful perfume consists of a complex formula with many exotic, luxurious ingredients, and the ultimate bouquet is in their subtle integration. At first you will smell one note, then another and the confluence of ingredients will flirt with your nostrils as you try and identify them. This is a pleasurable experience for you and for whomever is next to you. If you invest in a beautiful perfume, give it the honor of singing its fragrant song. It's not a good idea to have inexpensive, (possibly) synthetic or 'cheap' fragranced body or hair products competing with it!

What are the best fragrances for each season?

There is a reason why we wear lighter clothes in summer and heavier in winter, and fragrances have the same type of resonance. I am a firm believer that if you have found a fragrance that you love, and one that really suits you such as your own 'bespoke or custom' fragrance, then you can wear it all the time as your 'signature scent.' However, if you are always on the lookout for the latest fragrance just launched, which might be stronger or deeper and you wear it just because it is the newest, it might not suit your body chemistry, and could be a disconnect as well. Wearing lighter fragrances in summer and heavier fragrances in winter also have to do with comfort, climate and ***being considerate!***

Spoiler Alert! Have you noticed that certain synthetic fabrics such as polyester don't absorb perspiration and are water–repellant, which means that perspiration builds up inside the garment, hence the 'body-odor'! Make sure you wash or dry-clean synthetic fabrics after each wearing, because heat activates odor, and while you may not think your clothes need to be cleaned, the offending odor will confirm that indeed they do!

Understandably, it's not a great idea to wear a heavy fragrance in the summer. It will turn "cloying" on you and be unpleasant for those unlucky enough to be near you! On the other hand, a spring scent in winter might seem out of place, not to mention, inappropriate. In some ways, just the way you wear suitable seasonal clothes, you need to find scents that match the season, and you, so your scent is a celebration and in synch with the mood, climate and temperature around you. The following is a seasonal breakdown.

Spring scents are hopeful and fresh. The birds begin singing.

I love Spring! The warm sunshine feels so welcome on our skin and melts away our winter blues. Colorful blooms are popping up, and it's the perfect time to start planting the garden. New seasons herald new beginnings! Spring is all about sparkling, citrus scents—refreshing bouquets of aromatic lemons, limes, bergamot, neroli (the fragrant flowers of the bitter orange tree) and of course grapefruit—the bitter aromatic citrus scent with a distinctive undertone, reminiscent of black currant grapefruit. Ahhh! the lovely scent of Spring Blossoms after rain. The best perfumes for this season are scents that reflect festivities and flowers that smell like Spring: fresh, green, exhilarating, effervescent with a gauzy, gossamer top note that lures you in, coupled with fresh light florals—lily of the valley, magnolia (creamy, velvety and exotic), narcissus, tulips and herbaceous scents like mint and a rosemary "Fresh and Clean"—which is most Americans tell me they prefer! These are a few of my favorite Spring quotes!

“Can words describe the fragrance of the very breath of Spring” —Neltje Blanchan

“SPRING is Nature’s way of saying LET”S PARTY”
—Robin Williams

Summer flowers are fruity and flowery.

Summer is a time for outdoor romantic weddings and all kinds of florals ranging from light, to fruity to luscious floral scents and enticing robust flavors. Rose is a winner in summer, as are lilies, gardenias, jasmine, mandarin and ylang-ylang (an aphrodisiac with other healing traits), freshly mown hay, and crisp sun-kissed ocean air, barbecues, watermelon and coconut. All the delicious berry and exotic fruity scents are tempting—strawberry, blueberry, raspberry, pineapple, mangoes, lychees, vanilla (always a crowd-pleaser). This is a particular heady time for edible, gourmand scents. When you blend these together, you get a scent-ual bouquet of seductive full bloom scents—glamorous, colorful and exotic aromas. ***If laughter was a scent, this would be it.***

There is nothing that reflects the Scent of Summer more than the invigorating, fresh, sprightly "wake-up", sporty, crisp, natural newly-mown fresh cut grass and lovely scent of Summer flowers after rain. So, as you ponder about what notes to wear this Summer—think about how you want to feel and find the notes, and scents you love and don't be influenced by the latest celebrity or designer launch. If you love Rose, and it reflects your personality then find the best Rose perfume for you. Or if you love fruity notes, then find the one you love. And if you truly want to be original then you can combine the notes you love and create your own.

Shakespeare's sonnet "Shall I compare thee to a Summer's Day" is a beautiful tribute to this marvelous season! You may have had to memorize it in school, but here it is again, for you to enjoy.

Shall I compare thee to a summer's day? (Sonnet 18)
William Shakespeare—1564–1616

Shall I compare thee to a summer's day?
Thou art more lovely and more temperate.
Rough winds do shake the darling buds of May,
And summer's lease hath all too short a date.
Sometime too hot the eye of heaven shines,
And often is his gold complexion dimmed;
And every fair from fair sometime declines,
By chance, or nature's changing course, untrimmed;
But thy eternal summer shall not fade,
Nor lose possession of that fair thou ow'st,
Nor shall death brag thou wand'rest in his shade,
When in eternal lines to Time thou grow'st.
So long as men can breathe, or eyes can see,
So long lives this, and this gives life to thee.

Cinnamon, Spice and "Fall things nice"... Thanksgiving pie?

For a few colorful weeks each year, vibrant summer green leaves turn to a panoply of Autumnal hues of rich oranges, golden yellows, ochre, russet, purples and deep enchanted emerald-forest-greens and voila! Fall Scents have arrived… and with them delicious, hearty combinations of exotic spices, pumpkins, cinnamon, sensual and tantalizing cranberries, mulled wine, smooth fruity pear, tangy cherry blossom, exotic spices, nutmeg, silky vanilla and white musk. Contrasting flavors and combinations of honey, ginger, golden amber and creamy caramel laced with cinnamon complement this ***Season of Thanks*** with an evocative fall smell of delicious edible concoctions. Just in time for autumn, notes of sunny jasmine, crisp bergamot and fresh orange blossom combined with cinnamon spice, redolent white florals at the heart of the fragrance, with base notes of vetiver, patchouli, and woods provide darker nuances. Today's perfumers are still trying to outdo Nature's original ***Master Perfumer*** with tempting new and magical aromatic combinations to get the distinctive scent of Fall. Experience confidence in a bottle! Fall fragrances are unapologetic. Sipping mulled wine or brandy in front of the fireplace is a bold way for warmer, spicier and mysterious brooding fragrances like tobacco, leather, tonka bean and incense to be the perfect scents for when the temperature takes a dip.

"Life starts all over again, when it gets crisp in the Fall"
—F Scott Fitzgerald

"And all at once, summer collapsed into fall."
—Oscar Wilde

Winter is time to be wrapped up in a warmer scent.

There is no such thing as a strictly 'Winter' fragrance, or ANY actual seasonal scent, but the kinds of scents we choose to wear in winter are naturally richer, a little heavier, deeper, stronger and warmer and usually mixed with base notes of vanilla, cedar, ambergris, musk, benzoin, coumarin, suede, chypre, moss, and of course patchouli. Notes of cedarwood, sandalwood, and amber remind you of the great outdoors and forests. Many woodsy winter scents tend to be counterbalanced with spicy ingredients and may have a hint of orange peel to brighten it up. Unique combinations of these will give a special warmth and cuddliness. A bold and strong fragrance that lasts a long time is ideal in winter. Some of these ingredients are traditionally used in Men's colognes, but as stated earlier, any of these ingredients can be worn by men or women.

"You are the summer of my winter
Fragrances of your words
Radiance of your soul
Warmth of you heart color the life-Sun
I find myself in you and you in me" —Jugni

Anyone who thinks fallen leaves are dead has never watched them dancing on a windy day" —Shira Tamir

There are scents for night, scents for day.

What makes certain fragrances appropriate or inappropriate for certain times of day and night? Wearing a sophisticated fragrance with a heady floral sensual note (perhaps gardenia and ylang ylang) is perfectly acceptable at night—even desirable. It's a time to be flirty, provocative, sensual and sexy. You wouldn't wear that type of fragrance during the day or at the office, unless you wanted to give a 'different' impression! So, stay fresh during the day with lighter, more subtle energizing and refreshing scents with less of a sillage, and possibly mix it up with a hint of spicy notes during the day. There's nothing more lovely than a sparkling fragrance that exudes your personality, is revitalizing and refreshing and ideal for the day. As you walk by someone, they will be captivated by the scent and you!

Spraying perfume in the air is truly a waste!

I always say that Perfume is meant to be worn on clean, unscented moisturized skin. After your bath or shower, it's the best time to apply unscented moisturizer on your skin. Your body acts as a wonderful canvas and by spraying your fragrance all over your body (remember those pulse-points!) your fragrance will absorb, last longer and diffuse more. Your perfume is not an air freshener so don't go for the spritzing-in-the-air routine by walking into it. It's a waste of money and your beautiful, expensive perfume will land on your shampooed hair and even be distorted. If you're at a store, ask the salesperson if you can try it on your skin, on your wrist or arm so you can really smell the notes, and see how it mixes with your skin. Then wear it for a little while to see how the middle note releases, rather than making a decision on the top note alone.

How can you tell if a fragrance is right for you in a store?

Fragrance Sales assistants at stores promote their fragrances, not really knowing how it will match with your personal body chemistry. Despite a lot more information on the internet, most consumers have very little idea which ingredients are in a perfume and so when the salesperson says, "Try this and that," or " This is the latest…the newest….the best …the most original"… and the customer doesn't have a lot of time or really know the concentration and construction of the perfume they may like it at the beginning, but two hours later, mixed with their own body chemistry, they may hate it. Even if you know what some of the ingredients are, the middle and base notes may include an ingredient which you hate, eg. Amber or Tobacco are base notes and they only develop 2-3-4 hours later, and then you know what happens when you get home? Your aunt, friend or neighbor gets the perfume! And you are a very unhappy customer!

Want a new perfume but the stores are closed or in lockdown?

As we are now in a new reality of staying home more, you don't have to leave the comfort of your own home to hit the right note. These days, more and more companies are ramping up their online businesses, becoming home-based and offering fragrances online. Understanding that we don't yet have ***'scent-a-vision'*** (but it's coming) there are ways to actually discover your Perfume Personality Persona and take an "online fragrance journey;" have your results analyzed and receive a custom curated bespoke perfume just for you in the mail. In this age of 'selfies' everyone is becoming their own 'brand,' so you don't have to wear what everyone else wears. You can totally create your own.

A little self-promotion here. Long before social distancing and current home-based businesses became the norm, we've been creating custom fragrances for our clients, who inquire about the possibility to 'create your own scent' and they contact us. We began to offer corporate, teambuilding and perfume parties more than 12 years ago, and then at our lovely perfume studio The Scentarium in New York City. I heard several comments, with a chuckle, like *"What are you doing?... Tupperware parties for Perfume?"*

As more and more people are turning to self-improvement and reflecting their individuality, they also want their OWN custom fragrance and more and more fragrance lovers are reaching out through online search engines such Yelp and Google.

Even if you don't have an idea of the perfume you like, there are so many sites where you can search for fragrances and identify the type of perfume that most appeals to you, for yourself, or to buy as a gift for your significant other, loved one, or even a friend.

Americans are obsessed with cleanliness!

After creating fragrances for thousands of fragrance lovers, I can say with certainty that there are cultural differences which determine a fragrance's popularity; eg The British like very light crisp floral and lavender fragrances; South Americans like heavier Fresh-Floral-Orientals, European men and women enjoy richer Florals with Amber-Spicy notes; Middle Eastern cultures prefer heavier Ouds, Ambers and Musky notes, Japanese don't really wear fragrance but they love to *gift* it as a 'status' symbol. Americans are obsessed with sanitization and cleanliness and want "fresh and clean" scents. What does 'fresh and clean' smell like? It's so much more than just the scent of lemon –it's the delicious liquid rainfall smell that cools you after a steamy, stifling, sweltering day; it's the smell of fresh cut mown grass and morning dew, the salty marine sea air, the crisp breezy mountain air; all these scents are light, exhilarating and invigorating, and are 'fresh and clean".

Millennials have their own particular preferences.

Millennials love rare ingredients and like them to be natural and organic. Fresh, light and clean are a favorite and some want a 'no-fragrance-fragrance'. Millennials are very aware of innovative and unusual curated combinations and hence they buy perfume with a deeper awareness. They will go for boutique brands and are willing to pay a higher price for them and choose scents that they feel are environmentally-enhancing or may have healing properties.

Does a women's age influence her fragrance choice?

When we come across a perfume which our mothers and grandmothers wore, we immediately associate it as an 'older' woman's fragrance. However, when they were young, the trend was for powdery floral scents such as **Chanel No. 5, Joy, Arpège, Fracas** and they might still love wearing the scent of their youth. Interestingly older people tend to lose their acute sense of smell, and powdery strong scents are more distinctive, and so for those two reasons they prefer to wear fragrances which they remember from their youth and which they can still enjoy! As a rule, though, as we age, our sense of smell is diminished and that's why 'older women' tend to like heavier perfumes.

While some magazines used to limit a scent-strip to one per issue, to avoid 'competition' between fragrance companies, it was so popular that the decision was rescinded because the 'sampling' device became a lucrative revenue source for the magazines, as the fragrance manufacturers had to pay an "insertion" fee and also foot the bill for the scent-strips, in the millions, depending on the magazine's circulation. This is definitely a new take on 'stop to sniff the roses.'

There are times not to wear a scent.

Some gyms prefer that you do not wear your scent since there are people who claim to be allergic to scent. Hospitals may not be a good place, since people's senses can be askew when very ill. And when you go for your annual checkups, and mammograms the nurses require you not to wear deodorant or scent either.

SCENT ALERT: It probably is wise not to wear a seductive scent with your ex-husband or best friend's husband ... but I leave it up to you!

Wearing nothing but a scent

We've all heard the quote from the Queen of Glam, **Marilyn Monroe,** who famously proclaimed, ***"What do I wear in bed? Why, Chanel No. 5, of course".*** If perfume was a staple in her night-time routine, then you know it's worth having in yours. So, what kinds of fragrances do you like for bedtime? Many people confuse aromatherapy with perfume. Lavender is frequently mistaken as a floral scent. Lavender is a herb and most commonly used in aromatherapy. The fragrance from the oils of the lavender plant is believed to help promote calmness and wellness. It's also said to help reduce stress, anxiety, and possibly even mild pain. That is why many people use Lavender at night to sleep and to relax, but to wear Lavender as a scent alone can be a little daunting, as some lavender can smell a little like household scents.

I don't know too many women who *don't* wear perfume, but I have heard of plenty of men who proclaim proudly, "I don't wear anything"! I also think that pronouncement stems from an overzealous belief that their own body aroma (or is it odor) is masculine, appealing and sexy. Good hygiene is key to having good relationships, both personal and in business, and as long as daily cleansing, showering and deodorizing is practiced, then someone's natural body chemistry might be appealing. But remember my earlier comments, about perspiration being trapped in fabrics? Truly there is nothing more off-putting than someone who has NOT used anti-perspirant or deodorant, and at the end of a long day, it can be off-putting if someone relies only on their 'natural' essence!

Your personal notes:

Create your own

Scenting your own Image

Influencers have been considered the new celebrities and as a result, what they wear, how they talk, what they recommend and products they post becomes a major part of their image. Never before has creating your own image been as important as in today's new social media world. Whether you're an influencer or not, in the age of Zooming and Skyping, creating your own image is now one of the most important visual factors in this new Age of Corona. You don't have to be an "Influencer" and yet how you look, talk and sound on social media will certainly influence the success you achieve.

When I worked for Elizabeth Arden as National Training Director **Lagerfeld for Men** was one of our fragrance brands. We developed an innovative "Image Update" event/contest entitled "In Search of the Lagerfeld Man" as a national in-store promotion, to generate awareness of the fragrance and to appeal to men. It gained popularity throughout the country as men began to update their looks with our grooming products to create their own image. I was the spokesperson and helped them with their grooming needs in department stores, and literally updated and created a new image, by shaving, cutting hair, applying moisturizer, beard softeners, and bronzers. This was revolutionary at the time. Men in Department Stores permitting us to apply grooming products and to reshape their hairstyle? That wouldn't happen these days as we are all socially distancing and masking! However, we're in the age of Social Media where everyone has the opportunity to express themselves and to create their own image and their own unique brand on their own channel!

What's the advantage of a signature scent?

Wearing a "signature scent" is your way of leaving a mark everywhere you go and means that you have a fragrance you love to wear which represents you and reflects your individuality. When you wear "your" scent, people identify it with you. When you find and discover your own scent it instills confidence in you. It says, "This is who I am." When women fall in love with their signature scent, they typically wear it for years as it truly becomes part of their DNA. So, imagine their disappointment when it is discontinued and they can no longer find it? I cannot tell you how many times people call us to say their signature scent has been discontinued, and their sense of loss is palpable. Thankfully, we try and help them choose the notes they love and help them recreate their scent or even start by building something new. Over the years there have been many actresses whose name was linked to a scent—most famously Audrey Hepburn's perfume was L'Interdit by Givenchy, made for her in 1957. The perfume's name means "forbidden" in French.

You're your own Brand. Why wear what everyone else wears?

Personalization is possible in all product categories: jeans, tote bags, even DIY salads, or hair color—all of these are becoming the *thing*. As everyone discovers new beauty products and becomes a critic with prolific posts online, on Youtube and Instagram channels, we ***all*** have a voice. And we are all in charge of our own brand and Scent Persona. Creating your own perfume is not as difficult as it may sound. It just means finding a knowledgeable fragrance expert (moi!) and together (either online or in person) I help guide you to select your favorite notes, and voila! Your scent is really YOUR scent. Why wear what everyone else wears, when you can truly create your own?

Creating your own blend by selecting 4 or 5 favorite notes, is a growing popular trend and what we offer to clients and fragrance lovers.

Cleopatra's signature scent.

Cleopatra's perfume was so legendary that Marc Antony could supposedly smell the queen from miles away before her ships even arrived on the shores of his kingdom. The ancient perfume formulas that the researchers cooked up as Cleopatra's scent, based on the amphorae they have unearthed (antique perfume bottles), used a base of myrrh (resin originating from a tree native to the Horn of Africa and the Arabian Peninsula) along with several other ingredients that you might well have in your kitchen cupboard today, like olive oil, cinnamon and cardamom. Apparently, her ancient perfume gave off a nice musky, spicy scent that would last longer than most modern perfumes would.

Iconic people who wore distinctive perfumes.

Jackie Kennedy's perfume had style, like her.

Jackie Kennedy reportedly loved **JOY**, which was created with a lot of care, just like a Haute Couture dress, and thus it was extraordinary and timeless. It was presented by **Jean Patou**, as the most expensive perfume right at the time of the great depression in 1929, when the market of luxury fashion crashed, and the company could only survive on its perfume sales.

It's ironic that Jackie shared a predilection for her antagonist's scent; Marilyn Monroe also favored this classic rose and jasmine perfume by French couturier Jean Patou.

JOY is created with rare flowers in a unique concentration of 10,600 flowers of jasmine and 28 dozen roses which adorn the exceptional heart note of this perfume. With time this became the second best-selling perfume of all time (number one is Chanel No. Five.)

Intense and luscious with alluring floral composition, it starts with a fragrant tuberose, luscious rose, ylang-ylang blossom, aldehydes, sweet and mouthwatering pear and green notes. There is a spicy and darkened iris root. The base whiffs with sensual musk, warm and milky powdery sandalwood and mild, musky civet tones. Joy is a festive celebration of graceful floral aromas and the seal of good taste.

A perfume was named for Sophia Loren, but did she wear it?

Sophia had a variety of fragrances she wore, perhaps the first 'wardrobe' of fragrances, such as: Creed's **Irisia**, Emanuel Ungaro's **Diva** perfume, a full and powerful perfume, brimming with a floral citric aldehyde opening of bergamot, hyacinth, coriander and rosewood. The heart of this perfume is the honeyed rose core, flanked by indolic jasmine, tuberose, and ylang-ylang, with narcissus and iris. Overall, this is a classic perfume lover's perfume, and a classic rose patchouli lover's dream. Once upon a time this would be a formal event perfume, but you know that anything goes now! She also loved **Cabochard by Grès** (as do I). Since she was no shrinking violet this wouldn't have been too bold for this magnificent woman. Revlon's **Intimate**—a civet-drenched beauty which was considered hot stuff in 1955. Lancôme's **Magie** (La Collection Fragrances). She'd have worn the original, of course, in the evening, with fur. All these are in the Chypre family—bold, patchouli, oakmoss with floral-oriental notes.

It stands to reason. She was a sophisticated, sensual Italian actress with dark hair and smoldering eyes and lips… no light fresh and clean florals for her. She eventually licensed her name to Coty fragrance inspired by the famous Sophia Loren, an icon of style, femininity, grace and elegance. The perfume was launched in 1981 as an oriental floral, with dominant notes of jasmine and rose at the time of the start of the celebrity fragrance craze.

Lesson here: Just because a celebrity name is on a perfume, don't think they wear it.

Kate Middleton likes something pretty, like her.

The quintessential English Rose, Kate allegedly wears ***Jo Malone's Orange Blossom***, which has notes of citrus leaves, clementine flowers, lemongrass, white lilac, lily of the valley, orange blossom, waterlily, iris, vetiver and oak moss, and apparently likes it so much that she has it in candles also. For her wedding she wore ***White Gardenia Petals Eau de Parfum by Illuminum***, which sold out pretty much instantly once it was revealed to be the royal wedding fragrance. England's future queen is a floral girl, and this is clear from the feminine way she likes to dress.

Michelle Obama likes a delicate perfume, too.

The former First Lady, is a woman of style who has a unique taste for things, and some of the fragrances she likes to wear are ***Creed Love in White,*** a feminine fragrance inspired by Olivier Creed's travels on the high seas, "an element of nature that connects all humanity," and according to Creed, the bottle evokes "the shoulders of a feminine figure as she rests upon white sands caressed by the ocean's gentle current. "The top notes are Spanish orange zest, middle notes are magnolia, iris and jasmine, and the base notes are vanilla, ambergris, and mysore sandalwood. The perfume has an effect of delicacy and reassuring gentleness. Michelle also likes **Coty Vanilla Musk,** and Creed **Acqua Florentina** Perfume a fruity scent which is a youthful scent with sweet, fruity and citrusy notes.

What does handsome and talented as Hugh Jackman wear?

Known for his multi-faceted roles as an actor, singer and entertainer, **Hugh Jackman** has an equally eclectic collection in the fragrances he selects: **Zents** fragrance, **L'Artisan Parfumeur Timbuktu**, and **Tom Ford Vetiver**. Zents is a warm and buttery blend of vanilla, sandalwood and amber, laced with top notes of blood orange and grapefruit. From these it is clear that Hugh likes a clean smell, with just a touch of mystery. Tom Ford Vetiver is made up of citrus, rich spices and prized woods. Same thing—fresh and just a touch of sensuality.

Will Smith likes scents with a touch of tobacco and spice!

Will is known for wearing **Vera Wang for Men**. The scent is a classy, balanced oriental-spicy scent that exudes quality. The opening spray begins with a citrus note of yuzu, along with the unusual mandarin leaf greenness. The heart reveals a delicate anise touch, paired up with a moderate strength note plus tasty nutmeg spiciness. The sandalwood is high quality, immediately enveloping the scent with creamy exotic goodness. Tobacco adds a nice smoky touch, sealing the deal. What a real man would wear.

Your own signature perfume made for you is called bespoke.

An item that is "bespoke" means it is crafted personally for YOU. A bespoke perfume is created with your personal selection of ingredients created exclusively for you. In the past, a Bespoke Perfume was the domain of the very wealthy or royalty and would take anywhere from one year to two for perfumers to source the ingredients and then to actually compound them and finally to actually create the perfume. It was very expensive and not at all for the masses. We have been able to simplify the process somewhat and make it more affordable, yet still highly experiential and individualized. I take you on a "fragrance journey" and guide you through 18 perfume blends, and we evaluate the blends and ultimately you select the few that you love.

Everyone's taste is different, naturally, since we all have our own unique DNA. When you select the blends you love and combine them into your Bespoke Perfume, the results are palpable. Your own particular psychology and personality are uplifted by the combination of the unique ingredients you selected, and voila, you have your own evocative signature scent that no one else in the world has! It is gratifying to know that over the past 12 years, since we began our Custom Fragrance initiative in 2009, we have had over 16,000 people create custom fragrances and 45% are men. More and more men are creating their fragrances with one or more floral blends in their formula.

Interactive Educational Scentertaining® experiences online

Research shows that as many as 1000–1500 new fragrances are launched every year and those are just the ones we read about! There are so many 'niche' companies launching fragrances on the internet, and consumers are looking to learn more about them and gain knowledge. One of the most important trends that consumers and corporations are seeking are meaningful educational memorable 'experiences.' People become more engaged when they can actually learn about and experience products and services authentically.

We've all become more innovative, and popular video chatting and conferencing platforms like Zoom, Skype and FaceTime are now the new normal for seminars and webinars. One of the challenges is to create a fragrance experience on these platforms without actually being able to *smell* the perfume blends! We continue to offer in-person events, and practice social distancing, and now have added virtual events to our roster. We take participants on an educational 'fragrance journey' by describing the ingredients, telling a story, so that they can envision the ingredients, and present an overview about fragrance and give our clients our Perfume Personality Profile™ quiz which helps reveal their Scent Personality.

People love having an interactive, educational 'experience' in the comfort of their homes, and eagerly await their Bespoke Fragrance which will arrive in the mail a few days later- thus extending the experience.

*It's been so much fun
creating fragrances for some
people you might recognize...
and more inside!*

My mom in her studio painting BLOSSOMS for Scented Pillows which I presented on QVC.

Mom and Daughter—In my first acting debut in South Africa 10 years old

"PETUNIAS" by Grace Phillips—one of my favorite paintings

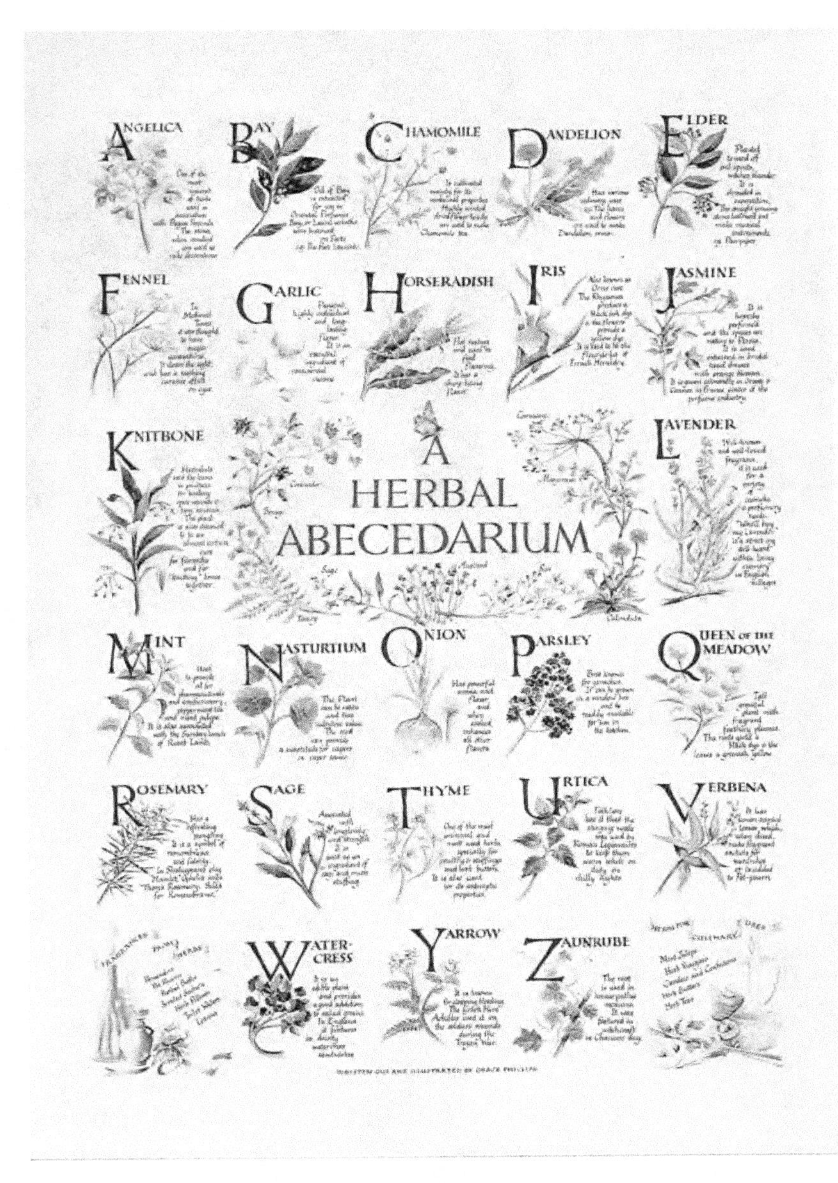

HERBAL ABECADARIUM by Grace Phillips—Calligraphy & Watercolor illustrations posters still available

CHANEL No 5—the iconic bottle created over 100 years. The bottle has remained constant but the logo and the cap has been modified over the years

OYSTERS are a powerful aphrodisiac—and they enhance the sense of smell—Food from the Gods!

4711 EAU DE COLOGNE—named after its street address in Cologne, Germany and one of the first Colognes ever marketed.

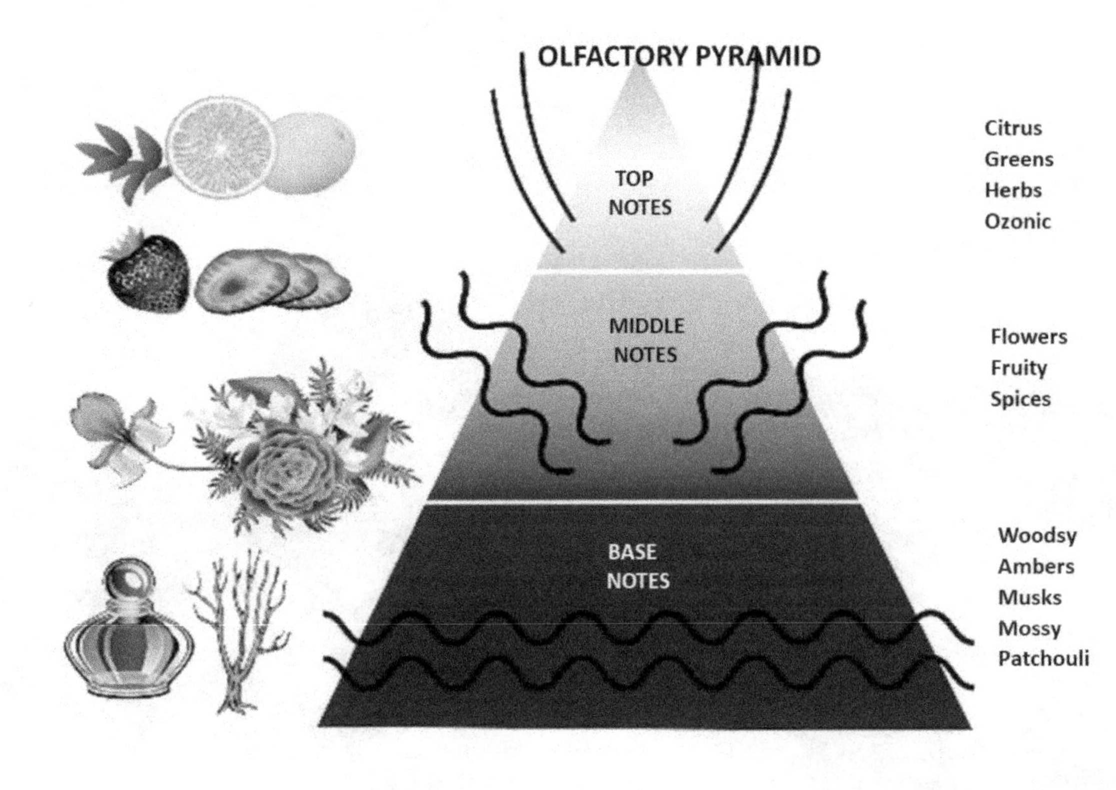

OLFACTORY PYRAMID—TYPICAL CONSTRUCTION OF PERFUMES

EGYPT STARTED IT ALL

SPICE MARKETS in the GRAND BAZAAR in MARRAKECH

SPICE MARKETS IN FEZ, MOROCCO

OPIUM By Yves Saint Laurent caused a major furor for glamorizing the idea of opium use! It was, and still is, a very popular perfume launched in the late 1970's.

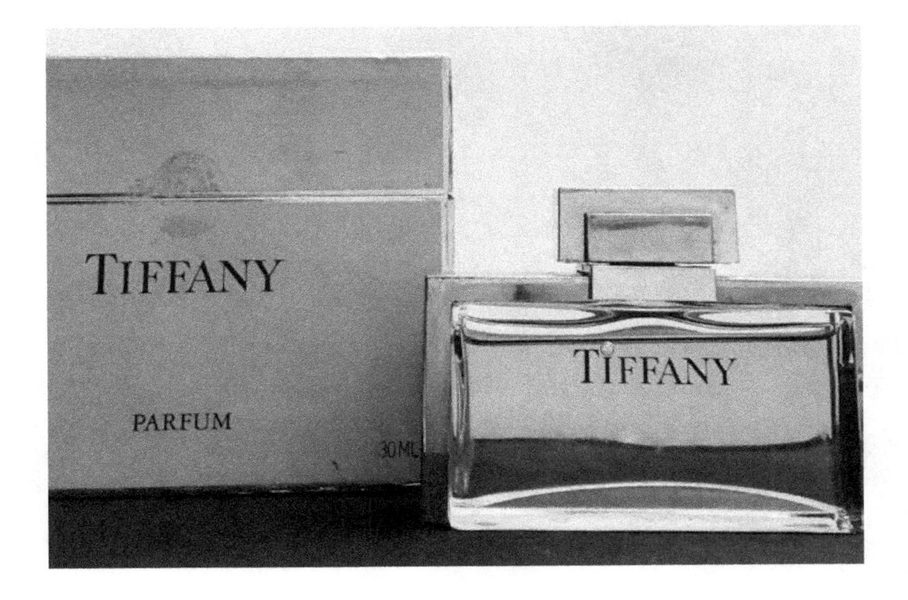

TIFFANY by TIFFANY & Co PERFUME. A luxurious, high quality, floral perfume with jasmine, ylang-ylang, bergamot with a woodsy amber sensual and sophisticated dry down. The ingredients reflected the quality of the brand and was created by Jacques Polge with whom I was honored to have collaborated in the lab in Paris. It was so exciting to have developed and launched the first Tiffany perfume as Executive VP Tiffany, Fragrance. Can you spot the diamond?

The bottle was designed by Pierre Dinand and was based on the art deco architecture of the Tiffany Building on 5th Avenue and 57th Street, with crystal glass for the bottle, and silver metal housing the bottle with a gold cap – reflecting the materials and luxury offerings that Tiffany is famous for, and of course the Robin's egg blue iconic packaging.

And what about MEN? The men's market has grown as celebrities, designers, and influencers are launching fragrances almost daily. The one enduring men's cologne is one that many of our fathers and grandfathers worE... do you remember what it was?

OLD SPICE was originally marketed and targeted as a woman's fragrance and was released in 1937. It is still popular today.

Hard as it is to admit, some men do not love strong fragrances!

VANILA—the beautiful orchid plant delights the eye. The vanilla bean comforts us in so many ways no wonder vanilla is so loved by everyone!

It was so much fun meeting Jamie Foxx to help him discover the magic & mystery of scent! He is witty, charming, talented with a twinkle in his eye and a great sense of humour

Jamie Foxx came to The Scentarium—my first custom perfume boutique in New York.

Katie evaluating different perfume blends

Katie Holmes at The Scentarium enjoying her "fragrance journey"!

Katie loved her bespoke perfume and she made one for Suri as well.

Zendaya is charming, engaging and a wonderful sense of humour

Zendaya and her" bestie" Darnell with their fragrances

Lisa Vanderpump at the Bella White party; she loves rose and jasmine perfume and she created "Lisa"

Karen Huger—the grande dame of *The Real Housewives of Potomac* wanted to create a fragrance—and invited the other housewives to a "discovery" fragrance dinner...

I loved meeting Sarah Pribis—host of HQ trivia. She called her fragrance "Gratitude" and became very emotional as she described her feelings! Fragrance triggers memories and emotions—and the reactions are palpable!

Taryn Brown also became so emotional when she created her fragrance "Nolabee"—named for her grandfather! Read the story about why she became so emotional... here's a hint..."float like a butterfly, sting like a bee"

Snooki and J Wow were so funny. They were fascinated with the aspect of fragrance and really had a fun, interactive, educational, and Scentertaining® experience!

J Wow! (Jenny) is 5′9″ and Snooki is 5′2″ (the long and the short of it) they were wonderful, and loved their fragrances

Meeting talented women in business and creating fragrances for them is so exciting—especially when they're on TV and have an interview

Rita Cosby is a delight and has supported me over the years—coming to the opening of The Scentarium and many of our events. Thank you, Rita!

Vanessa Murdock of CBS did a wonderful interview and loved her custom fragrance

Lauren Glassberg of ABC TV created a fragrance which she named "Beau" after her son!

Always wonderful to see Linda G. Levy, president of the Fragrance Foundation!

Jean Shafiroff, philanthropist, at our fragrance bar at The Plaza Hotel charity event.

Famed perfumer Roja Dove—I always love seeing Roja when he"s in NY.

Broadway actors Orfeh and Andy Karl at The Scentarium.

It was an honor meeting the legendary Cicely Tyson and creating a fragrance for her. So blessed to have met her with her beautiful family.

Susan Sarandon at the pre-Oscars party!

Marcia Gay Harden created a gorgeous fragrance—just like her

Dreamy Jason Lewis from *Sex and the City* certainly lived up to the name of the show!

Sam Asghari created a custom scent and hoped that his girlfriend Britney Spears liked it!

Hakeem Kae-Kazim, actor, was thrilled to get his custom fragrance.

Actor Christian Isiah was thrilled to learn about different ingredients and was a joy to meet!

Tichina Arnold was fascinated about how perfumes are created!

Theresa Randle is an actress and gorgeous inside and out!

Obba Babatunde Oscar winner in S.W.A.T. waxed poetic about how much he loved our exotic rose perfume!

Actress Carly Hughes! So excited!

Actress Bresha Webb inquiring about recreating a discontinued perfume!

Annalynne McCord created an exotic spicy fragrance

Environmental Scenting

Multi-Sensory Branding with Fragrance

by Sue Phillips, President, Scenterprises, Ltd.

The Scent Marketing Institute estimates that about $50-$80 million was spent on scent marketing in 2006 and that the figure will reach almost $1 billion in the next decade. Today, there are many ways to experience scent outside of personal care by integrating scent into the luxury brand experience.

Multi-sensory branding with fragrance; ambient scenting, environmental scenting has been incorporated into retail, hotels, spas and is a way for consumers to connect with the brand or property.

It was so much fun being on the Action Bronson Show on Viceland with Emeril Lagrasse, Tiff Benson, Big Freedia, creating a sensory experience—with food, wine, music, painting and fragrance—and a lot of dancing.

Tiff Benson learning about our blends

From L–R—Big Freedia, Tiff Benson, Action Bronson, Yours Truly on *The Action Bronson Show*

Kevin Harrington—an original shark from *Shark Tank* created his fragrance!

It was an honor to be involved with the British company Burberry twice, once with Elizabeth Arden as national training director and we created "dress for success" and grooming seminars for men in retail stores and then launching Society by Burberrys.

Burberry fragrance launch and 'dress for success' event in stores and on TV programs.

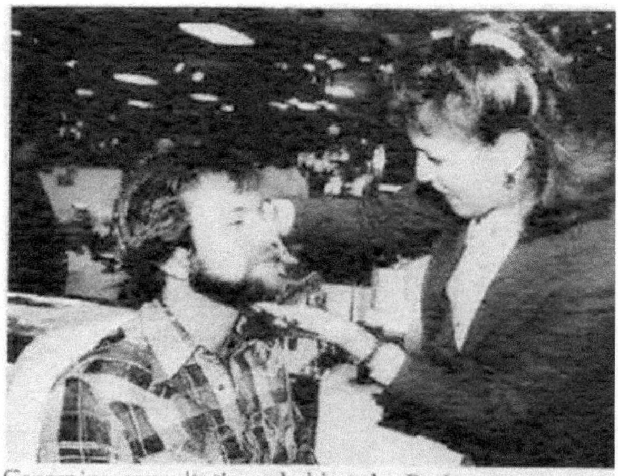

Grooming consultations, held at the Burberrys For Men counter, proved a strong sales

Grooming seminars for Burberry For Men by Elizabeth Arden fragrance launch—they loved it

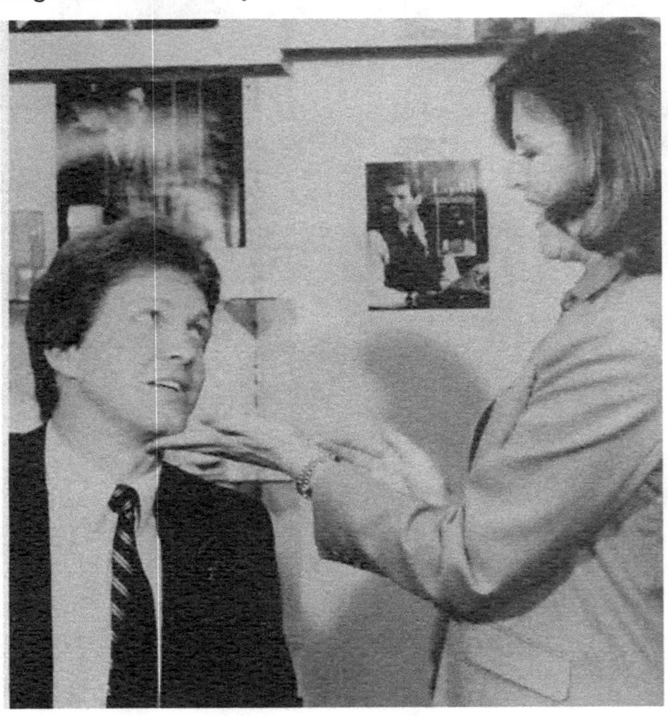

Bloomingdale's Chairman Marvin Traub enjoys the society of Royal Brands V.P./G.M. Sue Phillips, and Brigade Brands Chairman and C.O.O. Joe Venables.

***

I loved meeting the legendary chairman of Bloomingdale's, Marvin Traub, and launching "Society by Burberrys" was one of the most successful launches ever. We developed and launched a woman's fragrance for a predominantly 'men's brand. The elegant bottle with a red cap was designed by Pierre Dinand, and was based on the vintage toothbrush holders, that British used in their toiletry kits when traveling. The distinctive men's bottle with the blue cap followed the woman's launch.

Corporate "experiential" events are a wonderful way to promote team bonding and harmony. Citibank invited their private banking clientele for a hands-on custom fragrance event

Chantil and Charles had a great date night!

Fragrance lovers from Brazil celebrated their friend's birthday in New York & we are still connected.

One of my most memorable client events: two adorable young 6-year-old sisters were spellbound!

Thanks to legendary artist and playwright KEN FALLIN for this wonderful illustration and poster he designed for me! Thank you Ken!

Creating Bespoke Fragrances for Celebs

Jamie Foxx—Bespoke perfume gave the ultimate compliment

It is exciting when people and companies google-search for 'Custom Fragrances' and find us. I am so grateful to be able to do what I love, to meet amazing people, and to make a positive difference in people's lives, through fragrance.

One day I had just left my lovely perfume salon **The Scentarium** in Tribeca and received a call from a woman who was interested in booking an appointment for a 'certain celebrity'. I was intrigued and asked when she wanted to come in. Her answer was *"immediately"*. So, I suggested she meet me downtown and I gave her the address and retraced my steps back to my boutique. It turned out it was the assistant to "**Foxxy**" and he was interested in creating a fragrance for a lady love. (I had no idea who "Foxxy" was!) I explained the process and began the Fragrance Journey to create the fragrance. She and her friend enjoyed the session and said they would give the fragrance to her client for him to evaluate. The next day I received a call and was asked if I was available on Sunday afternoon to meet with 'him' as he wanted to 'tweak' it. **Jamie Foxx** arrived and is exactly as he is on TV and camera—charming, friendly, and so funny—he has an amazing sense of humor. It was so much fun working with him to adjust the fragrance he wanted to create for 'someone special'. I didn't ask him who it was but I did inquire as to what made him want to do the Fragrance Experience, and he said that he felt that gifting a Bespoke Perfume for somebody special was *the ultimate compliment* and reflection of affection. I couldn't agree more!

About 2 months later I received a call from Jamie's assistant saying that he wanted to book an appointment for 'the mystery woman' in Jamie's Life.

When she came in, I recognized her immediately. **Katie Holmes** is much taller than I realized, and she was really engaged in the whole process of taking our Scent Personality Quiz, and was intrigued with every aspect of the 'fragrance journey'. She really loved the fragrance that Jamie created for her and had heard about the 'experience' and wanted to go through the 'fragrance journey' herself. She asked so many questions and at the end, I offered, as my gift to her, that we make a custom fragrance for her daughter **Suri Cruise** and one for Jamie. And in doing research about what she likes, I know that she never gets tired of **Bulgari Pour Femme Eau de Parfum** which opens with bergamot and has violet and orange blossom. She wore **Clive Christian Number 1** to her first marriage. And now she has two *"Sue Phillips Bespoke Originals"*—one which Jamie made for her, and one which she created with me and which consists of a delicate floral with luscious fruity notes and deep sensual sandalwood and amber notes.

Zendaya Coleman, (known by her first name **ZENDAYA)** is a multi-talented young actress and singer and is down to earth, funny and really lovely. She and her friend 'Boy' (actually Darnell) came to The Scentarium to create a fragrance when she was in New York to film a series, and really loved the 'experience'. When it came to naming her fragrance, she mentioned that she was in NYC and then came up with the name **"NYZ"** and she and her friend and I, all agreed how perfect that was. Check out her response on youtube: https://bit.ly/3lBmmXb

One night I was coming into The Scentarium and a handsome gentleman was waiting outside. I asked if I could help him and he pointed to the entrance and said he was inquiring about the fragrance studio. I then realized who it was and was delighted to recognize **Laurence Fishburne.** I invited him downstairs, and he told me he knew what kind of fragrance he wanted. As he had another appointment at the Spa across the street, I wasn't able to give him the typical hour-long fragrance consultation, but based on what he requested I was able to select the blends he liked and in less than a half hour, created a terrific custom fragrance for him—a sophisticated, elegant, warm woodsy fragrance which was perfect for him.

Other celebrities whom I have been fortunate enough to meet and create custom fragrances for at the **Oscars Gifting Suites** are Oscar Winners **Marcia Gay Harden, Cicely Tyson, Susan Sarandon, Baba Obbatunde, Tichina Arnold, Jason Lewis** and nominees in some movies whose names I did not recognize, but it was certainly wonderful to meet them. I have realized that celebrities are just like you and me—they are absolutely thrilled when they find a fragrance they love! I have been in touch with many of them since, and they have been most complimentary about their fragrances.

...and then some of the *Housewives!*

I met **Lisa Vandepump** of **The Real Housewives of Beverly Hills** in the Hamptons at the annual Bella Magazine White Party and she loves Rose. I created an exotic Modern Rose Floral for her which she loved.

The Real Housewives of Potomac (RHOP)

I was contacted by **Karen Huger** who wanted to create a fragrance, and to unveil her latest 'discovery' at a dinner for all the Housewives, and to shoot the event for the RHOP series. She was embarking on a fragrance launch for her brand **'The Grande Dame'** and was in the discovery phase of developing a fine fragrance. She invited me to conduct a scent event and to discuss her new fragrance project. We connected both on a business and on a personal level as both our mothers had Alzheimer's—a cause about which Huger and I am passionate. The dinner started out beautifully, and everyone took our Perfume Personality Profile Quiz and I then analyzed their results and made a custom fragrance for each of them. While I was blending, Monique and Ashley got into a fracas and disagreed with one another, and then in true Housewives style, all hell broke loose! They literally began screaming at each other and so it was difficult to get them back to focus on their fragrances. Karen was really embarrassed and apologized to me profusely. You can see the melee on: RHOP: Monique Goes In on Ashley For That Four Drink Comment (Season 3, Episode 8) | Bravo

Sarah Pribis is an actor, host of HQ Triva

And utterly gorgeous and she came to The Scentarium and became so emotional when she ultimately smelled her fragrance creation which she called ***'Gratitude'***. She said she absolutely loved the 'experience', and she kept on getting emotional and said it was a lot more spiritual and personal than she thought it would be, and concurred that it is proof that our sense of smell connects to memories and feeling; it made so many feelings well up inside of her and there was a reason she called it "Gratitude'. I have all this on the video which is on my youtube channel: https://bit.ly/2KePwxL

So, take it from Sarah, as well, that fragrance really does connect memory and emotions, and when my clients encounter a scent that reminds them of something or someone, it becomes incredibly emotional. I have witnessed this so many times! Clients literally tear up and express themselves and reveal why their perfume is so meaningful for them.

Please view and subscribe: https://www.youtube.com /suephillipsfragrance

Nola Bee—Float like a butterfly... Speaking about emotions!!

A beautiful young woman named Taryn Brown created her fragrance and as she finalized her fragrance selection and applied it for the first time, she became very emotional and said she was so surprised as she doesn't get moved a lot as she is not an emotional person. She said it was so wonderful that she had a fragrance that reflected HER! I asked her what was she going to call it? She answered " I think I'll call it "***Nola Bee***"; and she explained with tears in her eyes that her grandfather, who was from New Orleans and who trained **Mohammed Ali** was the person who came up with the phrase ***"Float like a butterfly, Sting like a bee".*** So her fragrance was soft yet powerful and she said it was a 'family' scent now and her grandfather will be incorporated into her life every day now as she wears her fragrance.

Then Snooki and J.Wow!
The long and the short of it!

Two reality stars **JWoww** (Jenni Farley) and **Snooki** (Nicole Elizabeth Polizzi) who both came to prominence in the MTV reality series **Jersey Shore**, and were the main members of its spin-off, **Snooki & Jwoww** came to create their OWN perfumes as part of their "Moms with Attitude" series. Suffice it to say that they didn't really know a lot about fragrance, but they enjoyed the 'educational', interactive, fun SCENTERTAINNG experience and when I explained where Musk and Ambergris come from. Their response? *"Eeehyew!"*

I like to call their visit 'the long and the short of it" as JWoww is tall and elegant at 5'7" and Snooki is almost reaches 4'8" in heels. Though short in stature, Snooki couldn't be missed (especially with her pouf). Her party girl antics brought a whole new meaning to the term "fun-sized".

The Personality of Fragrance

Fashion and Fragrance— inner and outer accessories.

I always give the analogy that Fragrance is our *Inner accessory* and Fashion is our *outer accessory* and a signature scent reflects your heart, your essence your ethos! It's a way for others and you to discover who you are. It reflects your inner self, your inner beauty. You may look tomboyish but if your signature scent is a delicate floral, you are communicating that you are feminine, delicate, and you enjoy being a girl. Truly, though I doubt if a 'tomboy' would ever wear a delicate floral—it just doesn't seem to match with her DNA. But one never knows!! So, your scent may say something about you that is not obvious at first glance. It creates a dissonance that is interesting to the person who scents you! A signature scent may not always be what a person sees (or sniffs) at first glance when seeing you. It is your deeper self.

How perfumes and personalities match: What the carefree like.

Here's what I've observed. Someone who is carefree, casual and loves the outdoors will usually select a crisp, refreshing citrusy sent with light fresh floral notes of Lily of the Valley, Jasmine and bergamot. This olfactive category belongs to the "FRESH" family of fragrances and includes bergamot, and green notes such as fresh-cut grass, hyacinth, and watery or 'ozonic' notes—like the smell of the air after a rainstorm or a marine or oceanic scent. Fresh scents are refreshing and spirited just like a breezy Spring day.

What do sultry women wear?

Women with a little **Angelina Jolie** in them seem to prefer oriental/spicy scents which are all about sensuality, excitement and a flair for the exotic à la **Sophia Loren**. Spices, incense, vanilla, and musk are all used in this category as well as delicious food notes, such as chocolate and caramel. Oriental scents are warm, sensual, luxurious and a perfect complement to them is a red cashmere coat or a ticket to Paris or exotic Zanzibar. Interestingly enough many of the younger actresses today are into natural, outdoor, and lighter fragrances, while **Madonna**, known to prefer younger men preferably around 25, prefers **Fracas by Robert Piguet**—a very heady tuberose, (which she based her own ***Truth or Dare*** fragrance on) distributed by Coty and which was ultimately discontinued in 2015.

Real men like Florals too... Obba Babatunde is one.

Florals are the most popular family amongst women because they conjure up feelings of romance, and the flowers often appeal to people who are particularly in touch with their emotions. Floral fragrances also expand into fresh floral, light floral, fruity floral and "floriental" (floral/spicy combination). Don't be afraid to experiment with these. Some people think florals are old-fashioned because many decades ago, there were fewer options available, and perfumers used florals in abundance, and so florals were the 'parfums du jour', and Rose ingredients were also formulated into face powders—so our grandmothers applied them, and when we kissed them, we immediately encountered the rose scent.....hence Rose gets a bad rap as 'ol-fashioned'!

Floral scents can be soft and subtle like the scent of a rose garden. Or bold and exotic like the smell of lilies and gardenia. Interestingly, many European men have been known to enjoy Floral fragrances and seem to be more in touch with their masculinity by admitting to enjoy Floral fragrances! One of my favorite celebrities whom I met recently at the Oscars Gifting Suite is **Obba Babatunde** (born **Donald Cohen**, December 1, 1951) who is an American stage and movie actor, voice actor, producer, director and singer. He's also an actor on **S.W.A.T**. and ***The Bold and the Beautiful.*** **Oscar Winner at the Oscars Gifting Lounge loved creating his Rose Fragrance**

He selected my Floral blend and said "I am experiencing that which is loveliness in a bottle! This fragrance is absolutely sensational! He said "I chose the Floral because the moment I came here it spoke to me; it called me; it's absolutely welcoming, and that's what I always want to be".

What the romantic person likes...

That's easy, I bet you could have guessed it! A romantic likes a scent that doubles as the quintessential symbol of love: the rose. The ingredient of rose is becoming popular again, as it represents femininity and romance. My own **Exotic Modern Rose Perfume** includes notes of cognac, clove and Moroccan rose violet leaf and is the ideal combination of ingredients. It's a modern exotic fragrance that captivates and accelerates romantic moments. To increase playfulness and flirtatiousness in your life, consider a floral fragrance. Those with floral notes like jasmine, tiger lily and a slightly sweet undertone adds a hint of sensuality. A new Fragrance for Men and Women launched by Frassai's ***A Fuego Lento*** merges sweet and sultry, with a mix of orange flower, blackcurrant, and nocturnal jasmine to arouse the senses, culminating in a sensuous bed of balsam and suede. **A Fuego Lento** imparts an addictive, heady, sweet and sultry trail..." was launched in 2018. The nose behind this fragrance is Rodrigo Flores-Roux.

What the shy like...

As their personality type suggests, Shy people are usually demure and reticent, not wanting to be in the limelight. They prefer their fragrances to be soft, subtle and discreet, and welcoming notes of frangipani, green and white teas, cyclamen bergamot and sage are ideal subtle ingredients. Although it's often difficult to connect with someone more secluded, a particular perfume choice can also serve as an opportunity to bond. Gourmand notes of vanilla, saffron, gardenia, agarwood and magnolia blossom double as an aphrodisiac and will break down any social interaction. Guerlain's **Gourmand Conquin**, a fragrance with notes of black pepper, rose, smoky tea and chocolate reflect a sense of mystery as well as surprise in those who are introverted.

If you or someone you know is sporty...

You'll both like a light fresh scent that will go hand in hand with the active life of a sporty person. My own ***Fresh Tonic Sport*** is a crisp green blend and a typical men's sporty cologne; it's citrus green top note is reminiscent of an herbal tonic. **Juniper Berry** is the ingredient from which Gin is distilled and with bergamot and galbanum (an ingredient used in the 13th century used to ward off evil spirits) it is a typical men's perfume specifically catering to this personality; which is a ideal for diffusing due to its calming and grounding effects and ability to cleanse the air. But if someone you know is particularly competitive in athletics, try adding a touch of blue to their fragrance. "Blue spikenard, blue cypress, blue lotus or blue tansy will add a refreshing and chic hint of floral mint, perfect for any leader of the pack," states the perfumer, Mielo. ***Mielo Maroc Da'zur*** is a facial oi/perfume hybrid featuring the key ingredient Moroccan blue tansy, inspired by the blue colored Moroccan city of Chefchaouen.

If you or someone is a confident type...

Your tenacious 'confident' tendencies gravitate towards bold, strong notes that immediately catch one's attention. A distinctive heady scent like gardenia is narcotic, sensual confidence-building, and always a head turner! Our **Heady Floral Perfume** is a prime example formulated with gardenia, ylang-ylang, orange flower, carnation, and tuberose, and serves as a striking blend of scents. It is captivating and striking, evocative and sensual. However, if you are keen on bringing out a more vulnerable side to your self-assured nature, look into a fragrance with soft florals such as jasmine, mimosa and pink champaca. ***Magnolia* champaca**, known in English as champak, is a large evergreen tree in the family Magnoliaceae. More commonly known as Plumeria, it was previously classified as Michelia champaca. It is known for its fragrant flowers, and its timber used in woodworking. Plumeria alba is the national flower of Laos, where it is known under the local name **champa** or "dok **champa**.

Scent-Strips in magazine advertisements—are they effective?

What used to be regarded as innovative has now become overkill with as many as 8—10 'scent-strips' in a big issue magazine e.g. **Vogue** Sept issue. How did scent strips start? This actually started as a mistake (as do most brilliant initiatives) when a research chemist at NCR Corp was looking for an innovative way to prevent stains that remained in the company's cash-register tapes. His new process which produced tiny capsules of ink safely sealed in chemical bubbles eventually led to carbonless paper. Then 3M and NCR Corp working independently developed a new microencapsulation process that inspired 'scratch-and-sniffs' and ultimately fragrance strips. However, they used microscopic 'blisters' that contained SCENT not ink. What really catapulted this technology was in the early 1980's when Giorgio Beverly Hills introduced their very distinctive fragrance with perfume strips, as it was only available at their store. You may not remember but they inserted the scent-strip with an attached order form in several magazines and also in the remittance-envelopes of Retail Stores, e.g Bloomingdales, Saks and many others. The distinctive perfume and ease of the order form prompted an immediate sale plus a computerized data bank of that fragrance's customers with their addresses for future solicitation. At the end of the 80's the manufacturer had produced more than 500 million scent strips for the USA and foreign markets. It was incredibly lucrative for the magazines, the printing company, and fragrance manufacturers (with a relatively low cost to 'sample' a fragrance to millions of readers), pennies versus $2.00—$4.50 or more for an actual vial sample.

Ambient Scenting & Sensory "Experiences"

Scent-branding

One of the (not-so) 'new' trends to emerge, which is steeped in the rituals of the past, is the multi-sensory experience in which ambient or environmental scenting is fast becoming a way for companies to distinguish themselves from the competition and to 'scent-brand' themselves.

Today, environmental or ambient scenting is sophisticated and is fast becoming a multi-billion $dollar industry. Marketing gurus and scores of Fortune 500 companies such as hotels, spas, casinos, and retail stores are using scent as part of their marketing strategies to bypass competition and promote their brands, businesses, destinations, services or products. Scent Branding is an effective way to enhance customers' experiences, to influence future purchasing decisions and most importantly to establish an emotional connection with your luxury brand or business

What started out as a need to neutralize and diminish smoke odors from the Casinos in Las Vegas, almost 30 years ago, has become a way for these properties to utilize scent to offer a pleasant aroma and a positive environment for the guest, thereby increasing customer satisfaction, and at the same time 'scent-branding' their properties.

This has been backed by scientific claims done by researchers such as Dr. Alan Hirsch, director of the Smell and Taste Treatment and Research Foundation and Rachel Herz of Brown University. The Journal of Marketing and Journal of Retailing and Consumer Services has shown that scent can make shoppers spend more time and money in a store and make them pay more attention to a brand. Studies suggest that the right aroma at the right time can make people more likely walk up to a cash register and less likely to walk away from a slot machine (LA Times). Herz published a study in which she found that our senses all evoke equally accurate memories, but scents evoke ones that are more emotional. Many retail stores, hotels and luxury casinos have employed the usage of environmental aromas.

Research has found that scent marketing is done best when other types of senses are being examined as well. Places in which there is a high volume of lighting, texture, sound, and mood are also being utilized.

This has created a growing $750 million business. The industry is predicted to reach $1 billion within the next five years. The idea of scent marketing was also deemed one of Advertising Age Magazine's "Top Trends to Watch in 2017." The idea of utilizing scent marketing in a property that doesn't already have a scent is being incorporated in many public places. Hotels and casinos in particular carry a scent that has been engineered for the company that the customer won't experience anywhere else. It is a way of identifying a brand on a whole different level.

According to research in an LA Times article, Las Vegas casinos do use ambient scents (such as jasmine in the MGM Grand and **"Seduction,"** a signature scent, in the Venetian) but any connection between this and Hirsch's study may be circumstantial. "Scents are very effective in neutralizing and masking the smell of cigar and cigarette smoke," says Yvette Monet, a spokeswoman for MGM Mirage, parent of MGM Grand Las Vegas Resorts.

Research on scent aroma has shown increased productivity in the workplace and assists with health and medical issues. In Japan, factory workers have shown greater productivity when energizing scents have been pumped in and diffused in the factory air vents. If implemented correctly, the benefits of scent marketing can help a company to distinguish itself among competitors. It can help make an experience more unique and pleasurable for a customer. If customer satisfaction is the main goal of marketing, scent marketing is sure to become the new frontier in multi-sensory marketing.

Recently on a Delta plane to California I was delighted to discover a very pleasant aroma in both bathrooms—front and back. It was one of the first times I had ever experienced this and bravo to Delta for incorporating ambient scenting into an area which can be very 'challenging.' The delivery system was a scented removable porous 'hockey-puck type of pellet' which diffuses a very pleasant aroma in the air and is encased in a metal shell so that it stays affixed to the bathroom shelf.

Multi-sensory "experiences" for team-building events.

Studies have shown that powerful multi-sensory experiences motivate people, and corporations around the world are employing 'multi-sensory' experiences to engage, motivate and inspire their employees and their clients. As a result, employee *wellbeing* has been proved to significantly impact productivity and performance and employers are shifting their focus to the health and happiness of their workers. Incorporating and engaging ALL the 5 senses into the office space creates cohesivity and a brand-friendly environment that supports and promotes the company culture and customer experience. They might not remember what was said, but they will remember how they felt during or even after they left the event, or the workspace.

This is a new way of thinking for corporations. They organize seminars with music, food tastings, touching explorations, scent explorations and visual explorations. They bring experts in to help participants explore the POWER of the Senses, and amongst other activities, create a scent for each of their employees to help reflect their Individuality.

We have been thrilled to present Scent and Taste, Music , Color & Textures at Corporate events for companies such as Pinterest, Google, Lincoln Navigator as a few examples. They see these as enhanced team building activities since the senses stimulate new thoughts and even modify people's behavior by making them aware of what colors they choose to dress for different occasions, what music they listen to in order to relax or energize them, and of course fragrance to reflect their individuality and Brand Persona. The motivating factor is to offer a **memorable and meaningful event, experience and environment** and to instill confidence, positivity for long-lasting wellbeing, employee and client retention

Difference in Men's fragrances—Then & Now

Back in the 1700s, for example, Napoleon was known to wear an excess of perfume himself, which he'd use to cover up his natural and understandably strong body odor after months on the field.

Fast forward to recent times: In the mid to late 70s, when the perfume craze was happening for women, Fragrance Companies realized that the Men's Market' was another revenue opportunity and began marketing fragrance and 'grooming' products for men. So, products such as After Shave, Cologne, Beard Softening Conditioning Cleansers, Moisturizing Creams, Anti-Perspirants and Deodorants were all introduced and marketed. Typically, men's fragrance products were introduced at the women's fragrance counters, and many men were not as comfortable shopping there. Therefore, in order to generate interest and sales, the "Men's Fragrance Bar" was introduced in many Specialty and Department stores and many companies introduced 'In-Store' special events and PR campaigns to attract men to come to the counters.

In order to stimulate retail fragrance sales for Elizabeth Arden's two Men's brands, national PR campaigns were launched: "The Search for the Lagerfeld Man Contest" and the "Burberry for Men—Dress for Success Contest". In my capacity as National Training Director and Spokesperson for the Fragrance Brands, I was involved in both campaigns. Here I am in Chicago at Marshall Field's presenting Grooming Seminars and shaving men's beards while first applying beard softening conditioning cleansers, applying moisturizer, bronzers and appearing on TV with the Image Updates events. It was such fun and the men loved it. Sales soared!

Insights—words of wisdom

For centuries, Fragrance has been used in a myriad of ways: to seduce lovers, beautify ourselves, elevate our mood, enhance our environment, heal us; been used by worshippers in religious ceremonies, celebrate occasions, refresh our bathrooms, neutralize food odors, bring the outdoors inside.... It embraces all the senses: **Sound,** a fragrance might be harmonious or discordant, loud or soft, sharp or flat; **Touch**, it can be perceived as smooth or rough, soft, silky, cool or hot. **Taste** also gives many choices, especially since smell is so closely linked to the sense of taste. A scent can be salty, sweet, sour, bitter, chocolatey, yummy and fruity, to name a few edible and gourmand descriptions; and **Sight,** the visual sculptural delight of a crystal perfume bottle reflecting rays of light and housing the different colors of the actual perfume itself, which can go from a light golden hue to rich deep cognac and treacle colors—all a joy to behold.

Due to Covid, and more so than ever before, even after 9/11, we are desperately seeking **Comfort**, **Serenity, Calming**, **Happiness, Delight, Laughter, Communication, Optimism**, **Laughter, Gladness** and **Well-Being** because we have spent months at home, in isolation, not being able to be with loved ones, and seeing tragedy all around us. This sadly, will probably continue for a while longer as we continue to endure the new normal. Fragrance is definitely a way for us to bring comfort, refuge, safety, joy and happiness to us and our homes, and beautiful scents and home fragrances with candles, sachets, perfumed pillows, diffusers will certainly elevate and uplift our mood and environment and bring about a sense of contentment and cheerfulness to our daily lives.

How does fragrance make one feel?

I believe that of all our Senses, fragrance helps people feel confident, sexy, beautiful, happy, intelligent, and above all, it epitomizes an empty canvas upon which life "paints" our everyday feelings, moods, victories and tragedies. It reflects the images and textures that manifest on the canvas we create based on the life we lead, and how we land up feeling. Whatever our mood, whether we feel happy, sad, motivated, healthy, busy, or encounter difficulties, how we land up embracing life, either with happiness or suffering negative situations and tragedies—all will be evident on our 'canvas'.

The more commercial and noticeable symbols of beauty are the traditional, tangible and visible aspects of beauty, such as skincare, cosmetics, haircare and by using those tools and products that are available to us, we can transform our outer beauty. A new hair color, different hairstyle, brighter color lipstick, gold metallic eye shadow can uplift our spirits and 'beautify' us. Having a glam new updated look, will definitely make us feel different.

But to truly feel beautiful and uplifted on the inside, one of the tools I find that helps my mood a great deal is applying my exquisite custom fragrance. There is nothing more special than having a perfume that truly reflects your personality and individuality, and the ebullience, exuberance and total elation you feel when your mood is transformed is palpable.

The more positive and fulfilled life you lead, with self-care, proper diet, exercise and nutrition all will be reflected and if you are a happy, positive fulfilled, spiritual person, Beauty will be noticed and reflected on your 'canvas'. My philosophy about life and Beauty is to enhance what we were born with and to strengthen it with the marvelous tools of the trade that we have at our disposal. Starting from the inside, how you feel when you start your day will determine what colors, style and clothes you will want to wear. That is the perfect beginning which will complement your mood and reflect your outer accessory. To amplify and magnify your beauty, to enhance your wellbeing, to reflect your positivity and to exude joy is how you want to feel the entire day. To absolutely feel that way, without hesitation, your inner accessory, your signature perfume will enhance every aspect of your mood, and give you the inner confidence to say, "I look beautiful, I feel beautiful, I am beautiful, and nothing and no one can change that". That is my wish for me, for you and for everyone in our lives. To feel secure, beautiful and to feel the best we can feel, is what I believe fragrance can do for us.

In the same way that we enhance our eyelashes which are there to protect our eyes from sun and impurities, and we enhance them with mascara or false eyelashes, we see a tangible and visible difference!! That is the visceral difference I wish for all of us—to feel that our lives and beings have been transported to a much higher elevation of beauty, positivity and joy—all through the wonderful world of fragrance.

As long as commercial beauty ***enhances*** and doesn't detract from original beauty, then I am 'all in'! I believe that philosophy will help one feel uplifted, confident and empowered. And Fragrance? Fragrance is the quintessential barometer about how it makes you feel! Uplifted, Confident, Sexy, Sensual!

How to create self-beauty in your life?

I never leave my home without my perfume. if I change handbags and realize I've left my fragrance in my other bag, I have to go back home because I literally feel incomplete without it.

I have known to be late for meetings (!) but I would feel naked if I didn't have my perfume with me, and uncomfortable all the time!

Smiling and greeting people in an authentic way is a lovely way to elicit positive vibes. I also feel it is so important to smile and to acknowledge people with consideration and to always ask their names. When I am at a restaurant, I always ask the name of the server or waiters because I feel that that it is a sign of respect to address them by their names, as opposed to HEY YOU! or WAITER????

On a personal note, I try to do all the things we are supposed to do—but now and again I fall off the wagon and cheat with chocolate and other 'sinful things' but I love wearing perfume and give myself 'permission' to indulge, and NEVER leave home without it!

How to respond when given a compliment?

Accepting compliments gracefully is not easy, but imagine if the fragrance you love to wear gives you that boost of confidence? Then accepting a compliment is easy, right? As young girls we might have been raised to be polite, not to express our views (if they were controversial), to be feminine, and our 'Prince Charming" would whisk us off to the fairy castle. Well look how that worked for Megan!

We are in an exciting time where we are able to celebrate our differences and our individuality and by so doing we we don't have to wait for Prince Charming to find us......we can choose whether to have or not have a mate and to fulfill ourselves with the passion of our work.

Speaking of work, I was thrilled and honored to develop and launch **Society by Burberry**. The bottle was designed by iconic designer **Pierre Dinand**, representing an antique vanity and toothbrush holder. The packaging was feminine with the subtle plaid design in white which referenced the signature check and the red ribbon paid homage to the Burberrys scarf!

The fragrance was a fresh green crisp sparkling fragrance with lavender and Iris, and a nod to its British roots and hugely successful. We introduced it around the country and globally. A year later we followed it with ***Society for Men by Burberrys,*** a brisk, woodsy, chypre man's fragrance and thus began the love affair that the American market had for Burberry. The advertising campaign was shot by **Patrick Demarchelier** and it was a thrill to develop and launch this authentic global brand.

What drew me to the beauty business?

It started quite serendipitously. I never had dreams of being in the fragrance industry, but grateful to have had the opportunities that were presented to me. I had studied acting at school and always wanted to be in theater. In a strange way, I have utilized my performing skills by conducting presentations and speaking engagements and motivational programs to clients and also to my students as Adjunct Professor at **FIT College** and **LIM** College teaching fragrance courses to eager young fragrance students.

What I love to do...

I truly love that I make a difference in people's lives through fragrance. When they create a fragrance that really resonates with them and it 'speaks' to them, they literally well up with tears. It brings back memories, it reminds them of people they love, or situations they have encountered. I am blessed to have found my passion and it permeates my life. I am positive, and an outgoing person and like to help people.

My aim is to make a positive difference in people's lives by helping them discover their own unique persona, and by understanding their Olfactory personality. This builds confidence & wellbeing. Why wear a fragrance that everyone else wears when you can create your own? When asked what you're wearing? Your answer: "It's Special! It's Mine!" We promise that people will gravitate towards you because your own unique scent reflects your individuality and your confidence quotient will increase! Take our Perfume Personality Profile Quiz at the end of the book and we can create a custom fragrance for you.

It is strange to think that I have been in New York far longer than I was in South Africa and working in the Fragrance Industry has certainly been exciting and fulfilling. Having the opportunity to meet designers, celebrities and thousands of fragrance lovers who are captivated by fragrance and how it makes them feel is testament to the power of perfume.

From where do I draw inspiration?

Years ago, when I was going through a transition, I went for a run and listened to a powerful audio recording by the author and philosopher Eckart Tolle and the Book was **'Living in the Now'.** It certainly was a gamechanger for me.

His philosophy was, and I am paraphrasing it very simply:

"We can't ever go back to the past so don't dwell on what you cannot change"."

"We have no idea what the future holds, and shouldn't base our life on that"

"We only have the present! We must live in the Now".

This credo has shaped the last 30 years of my life! So, when I think about or have ideas for business opportunities, business challenges, or possibilities in my personal life, I seize upon them and I act upon them, because I never know if they will surface again. And what's the worst that could happen? They might not work out but something new will always arise!

I am grateful to the many people in the industry who have guided and supported me and to the late Jim Morton whom I met when I became the Fragrance Training Director at Elizabeth Arden. As part of my orientation into the fragrance world, I spent a day with him gaining insights into the competitive and complicated world of marketing and fragrance… and he said *"Sue, become a fragrance expert"*. I had no idea how to do that! So much has been written about Fragrance and the Art of Scent. This book is my homage to the many years I have spent in this industry and I hope you have enjoyed reading about this wonderful subject, and that you have gained insights into it and are inspired to experience it more fully.

I am grateful to my amazing clients for the opportunity to make a difference in their lives through our most powerful sense.

Live! Enjoy Life, Laugh! Love!

Live your best life and be SCENTUALLY YOU!

Scentfully,

Sue Phillips

Sue Phillips, born and raised in South Africa, is an author, Motivational Speaker, Fragrance Expert, Woman-owned business and Scentrepreneur®. Sue shares her expertise and knowledge to help individuals and organizations accelerate growth, promote wellbeing and empower their clients and employees to be the BEST they can be, through our most powerful sense! Sue has appeared on television and is an inspiring speaker. Ideal for Sales Meetings, Teambuilding, Corporate Events and Keynote Speaking engagements.

www.suephillips.com and www.scenterprises.com

Have you ever wanted to create your OWN Bespoke Fragrance? Take our Perfume Personality Profile Quiz™ to discover YOUR Olfactive Personality. This is ideal for both men and women. Take it yourself, or send this to a loved one or friend. Email your answers to info@suephillips.com and advise if this is for you or if it is a gift, and what fragrance/s you currently wear. If you would like to receive your very OWN Custom Fragrance or to send it as a gift, complete the answers below and email it to us, with a comment that you have read the book with the code PERFUME

Perfume Personality Profile Quiz™

SUE PHILLIPS

FRAGRANCE

SCENTERPRISES
NEW YORK

Check one answer which most applies to you:

Please select what gender your fragrance is being designed for:

Female:

Male:

Binary:

Tally your scores. Complete the box below that corresponds with your answers.

A's	B's	C's	D's
IIII	IIII	IIII	

1, Which of these fabrics do you prefer to wear against your skin?

A. Wool
B. Linen
C. Silk
D. Cashmere

2, Which artist inspires you most?

A. Michelangelo
B. Jackson Pollock
C. Claude Monet
D. Georgia O'Keeffe

3. What is your favorite season?

A. Autumn
B. Spring
C. Summer
D. Winter

4. If you were to build your dream home which of the following would it be:

A. Frank Lloyd Wright Prairie Home
B. Penthouse apartment
C. English cottage
D. Palatial mansion

5. Which drink would you most likely order when out with friends?

A. Dry, full-bodied cabernet
B. Vodka tonic
C. Orange-Blossom martini
D. Draft Stout Beer

6. What would be your dream vacation?

A. Escape to the redwood forest
B. Spring in Tuscany
C. A pampering spa getaway
D. Trekking through the Himalayas

7.To dress impactfully, which colors do you choose to wear?

A. Warm, earthy tones
B. Vibrant greens and turquoise
C. Pretty pinks and purples
D. Deep varieties of red

8.What is your favorite time of day?

A. Late at night
B. Early morning
C. Mid-afternoon
D. Dusk

9. You're happiest when you sniff?

A. An antique bookshop
B. The sea air
C. A flower shop
D. A bakery

10. Which would you be likely to own?

A. Polished mahogany table
B. An antique rocking chair
C. Limoges china
D. An Impressionist painting

11. Which icon do you most admire?

A. Cate Blanchette
B. Julia Roberts
C. Marilyn Monroe
D. Lady Gaga

12. Which male film icon do you admire?

A. George Clooney
B. Jamie Foxx
C. Bradley Cooper
D. Denzel Washington

SUE PHILLIPS

FRAGRANCE

SCENTERPRISES
NEW YORK

CUSTOM PERFUME FOR A GIFT:

RECIPIENT NAME ____________________

SCENT NAME ____________________

EMAIL ____________________

Instagram ____________________

TEL ____________________

BIRTHDAY ____________________

MESSAGE TO THE RECIPIENT FROM YOU

CUSTOM PERFUME FOR YOU:

YOUR FULL NAME Karina Page

NAME YOUR SCENT Katerina

ADDRESS 114 Capeberry Irvine, CA 92603

EMAIL Karinapage@mac.com

Instagram ____________________

TEL ____________________

BIRTHDAY ____________________

Any special notes: ____________________

CHECK TO BE PLACED ON OUR MAILING LIST ☐

Thankyou for taking our Perfume Personality Profile Quiz™ Please contact us at info@suephillips.com and follow us on Instagram: @scentfullysue; @scenterprises; @therealsuephillips; @thescentarium we will follow you back. Thankyou!

Scentfullly,

Sue

Famous Quotes about Perfume

"The beauty of fragrance is that it speaks to your heart…
and hopefully, someone else's."
—Elizabeth Taylor

"No elegance is possible without perfume.
It is the unseen, unforgettable, ultimate accessory."
—Coco Chanel

"Fragrances fill the senses with the mysterious."
—Diana Vreeland

"Forgiveness is the fragrance that the violet sheds
on the heel that has crushed it."
—Mark Twain

"Make me a fragrance that smells like love."
—Christian Dior

"A fragrance is a veritable story, told and explained in scent,
in notes, in impressions. It's a score based on the emotions of
each instant, a captivating music of the senses."
—Alber Elbaz

"A fragrance is like a signature, so that even after a woman leaves
the room, her fragrance should reveal she's been there."
—Oscar de la Renta

"Fragrance is so intimate for a lot of women—
it's your essence, your identity."
—Christian Louboutin

"Happiness radiates like the fragrance from a flower,
and draws all good things toward you."
—Maharishi Mahesh Yogi

"A bit of fragrance always clings to the hand that gives roses.
If you are generous, you will gain everything."
—Confucius

"A fragrance always combines femininity and sensuality."
—Gianfranco Ferre

"A woman's perfume tells more about her than her handwriting."
—Christian Dior

"A woman who doesn't wear perfume has no future."
—Coco Chanel

"Wear perfume wherever you want to be kissed!."
—Coco Chanel

"What do I wear to bed? Why, Chanel No. 5 of course."
—Marilyn Monroe

"Perfume follows you; it chases you and lingers behind you.
It's a reference mark. Perfume makes silence talk."
—Sonia Rykiel

"One of the very few things that I do every single day is put on fragrance. If I'm not wearing make-up, if my hair's not done, if I'm walking around in pajamas—I still put my fragrance on.
I will brush my teeth and put on my perfume."
—Blake Lively

"Perfume is that last and best reserve of the past, the one which when all our tears have run dry, can make us cry again!"
—Marcel Proust

"Perfume is like a new dress, it makes you quite simply marvelous."
—Estée Lauder

"Perfume puts the finishing touch to elegance—a detail that subtly underscores the look, an invisible extra that completes a man and a woman's personality. Without it, there is something missing."
—Gianni Versace

"Perfume must not be linked just to fashion
because that means that one day it will go out of style."
—Thierry Mugler

"Perfume is a mark of female identity and the final touch of her style."
—Christian Dior

"A perfume is like a piece of clothing, a message, a way of presenting oneself, a costume that differs according to the woman who wears it."
—Paloma Picasso

"No elegance is possible without perfume.
It is the unseen, unforgettable, ultimate accessory."
—Coco Chanel

"Ladies, a man will never remember your handbag,
but he will remember your perfume."
—Olivier Creed

"Long after one has forgotten what a woman wore,
the memory of her perfume lingers."
—Christian Dior

"Until I was a teenager, I used red pokeberries for lipstick and a
burnt matchstick for eyeliner. I used honeysuckle for perfume."
—Dolly Parton

"Beauty is an ecstasy; it is as simple as hunger.
There is really nothing to be said about it. It is like the perfume
of a rose: you can smell it and that is all."
—W. Somerset Maugham

"Love is a perfume you cannot pour onto others
without getting a few drops on yourself."
—Ralph Waldo Emerson

"He had preserved the best part of her and
made it his own: the principle of her scent."
—Patrick Süskind

CPSIA information can be obtained
at www.ICGtesting.com
Printed in the USA
BVHW042200120421
604793BV00016B/346